AQA

Make the Grade!

Understanding **GCSE** Geography
for AQA Specification

Controlled Assessment Student Workbook

David Payne Consultant

Heinemann
Part of Pearson

Name: ....

Understanding **GCSE** Geography
for AQA Specification A
Controlled Assessment Student Workbook

David Payne
Consultant: Brian Taylor

www.heinemann.co.uk

✓ Free online support
✓ Useful weblinks
✓ 24 hour online ordering

0845 630 33 33

Part of Pearson

Heinemann is an imprint of Pearson Education Limited, a company incorporated in England and Wales, having its registered office at Edinburgh Gate, Harlow, Essex, CM20 2JE. Registered company number: 872828

www.pearsonschoolsandfecolleges.co.uk

Heinemann is a registered trademark of Pearson Education Limited

Text © Pearson Education Limited 2010

First published 2010

12 11 10

10 9 8 7 6 5 4 3 2 1

British Library Cataloguing in Publication Data
A catalogue record for this book is available from the British Library.

ISBN 978 0 435 04377 3

Copyright notice
All rights reserved. No part of this publication may be reproduced in any form or by any means (including photocopying or storing it in any medium by electronic means and whether or not transiently or incidentally to some other use of this publication) without the written permission of the copyright owner, except in accordance with the provisions of the Copyright, Designs and Patents Act 1988 or under the terms of a licence issued by the Copyright Licensing Agency, Saffron House, 6–10 Kirby Street, London EC1N 8TS (www.cla.co.uk). Applications for the copyright owner's written permission should be addressed to the publisher.

Edited by Elina Helenius

Designed by Colin Tilley Loughrey

Typeset by AT Communication

Original illustrations © Pearson Education Ltd 2010

Picture research by Elena Wright

Cover photo/illustration © G.M.B. Akash/Panos Pictures

Printed in the UK

Acknowledgements
The author and publisher would like to thank the following individuals and organisations for permission to reproduce photographs:

David Payne, p.55, 56, 67; Greg Balfour Evans/Alamy p.56, 59.

The author and publisher would like to thank the following individuals and organisations for permission to reproduce copyright material:

p.23 'Loved to death', adapted from Loved not wisely but too well by Carolyn Murrow-Brown,14 April 2001, The Times; p.23 'Keep off the grass!' AQA examination questions are reproduced by permission of the Assessment and Qualifications Alliance.

Every effort has been made to contact copyright holders of material reproduced in this book. Any omissions will be rectified in subsequent printings if notice is given to the publishers.

Websites
The websites used in this book were correct and up-to-date at the time of publication. It is essential for tutors to preview each website before using it in class so as to ensure that the URL is still accurate, relevant and appropriate. We suggest that tutors bookmark useful websites and consider enabling students to access them through the school/college intranet.

© Pearson Education, 2010

Contents page

© Pearson Education, 2010

Section 1: Getting the most out of your Controlled Assessment

What is Controlled Assessment?

What contribution does Controlled Assessment make to your GCSE?

Controlled Assessment is the method used to complete one part of your GCSE Geography assessment. It is worth 25 per cent of your GCSE marks; the remaining 75 per cent of the marks are allocated to two written examination papers. Your final grade will be determined by putting together the marks awarded for your Controlled Assessment and examination.

What does Controlled Assessment involve?

Your Controlled Assessment task is called a **local fieldwork investigation**. This means that you have to investigate a geographical topic which is located within a small area (usually your local area).

Carrying out a local fieldwork investigation involves collecting information (data) and producing a short report of about 2000 words. Your completed report will be marked using a mark scheme produced by the Examination Board (The Assessment and Qualifications Alliance – AQA).

Why is it called 'Controlled Assessment'?

All three parts of your Geography assessment (The Local Fieldwork Investigation **and** two written examinations) are managed by the Examination Board (AQA).

The Examination Board gives strict guidelines about how the local fieldwork investigation must be managed. These guidelines are called 'Controls' and they operate at three levels (limited, medium and high levels of control). The Controlled Assessment process is made up of the following three stages.

Stage 1: Task setting (High control)

The Examination Board publishes a list of **task options** each year which are based on your Geography course. Each task option has a **task statement**. Your local fieldwork investigation must be based on one of the task statements. The task options and task statements change each year. The following table shows the 2011 task options and task statements.

Task setting is called 'high control' because the Examination Board has total control of the Task Options and Task Statements

Controlled Assessment - 2011	
Task options	Task statements
1 Rocks, resources and scenery	Investigate how a former quarry is used for the benefit of a locality.
2 Challenge of weather and climate	Investigate the weather features of the passage of a depression.
3 Living world	Investigate the issues relating to the management of an area of deciduous woodland.
4 Water on the land	Investigate how features of a river change over distance.
5 Ice on the land	Investigate how a glacial landscape is managed.
6 The coastal zone	Investigate a coastal habitat.
7 Population change	Investigate the impact of migration on locality.
8 Changing urban environments	Investigate land use in (part of) an urban area.
9 Changing rural environments	Investigate leisure opportunities within a rural area.
10 Globalisation	Investigate attempts at achieving sustainable development within a locality.
11 Tourism	Investigate a UK National Park or coastal resort as a tourist destination.

© Pearson Education Ltd, 2010

1

Important questions:

> *Do I have a free choice of any of the task options?*

Yes – However, in most cases schools will choose one of the options for their students in order to fit the Controlled Assessment topic within the general pattern of teaching for the whole course.

> *Does the title of my investigation have to be exactly the same as the task statement?*

No – However, your investigation must clearly reflect the idea expressed by the task statement.

Stage 2: Task taking (Limited and high control)

'Task taking' simply means completing your investigation. This will involve:

- collecting information
- presenting information
- writing about the information that you have collected
- reaching a conclusion
- evaluating your work.

- You will be allowed 20 hours to complete your investigation. This does not include the time you need to collect your information (data).
- Background reading and research can be done without supervision.
- Writing up your work **must** be done under supervision.
- During the task taking stage your work will be taken in after each session.

Task taking has a mixture of 'limited' and 'high' control.

Limited control [normal class supervision / help and advice from your teacher is acceptable]

- writing your introduction
- explaining your methods
- presenting your data

High control [formal supervision / no help or advice from your teacher or other students is allowed]

- writing your interpretation, conclusion and evaluation

Important points: During the high control stage:

- you can use your research notes but must not bring in any additional or new material
- you must work independently in order to make sure that this part of your investigation is totally your own work.

Stage 3: Task marking

Your completed investigation will initially be marked by the school and then moderated (checked) by the Examination Board.

> ### Good Advice
>
> In most cases schools will organise task statements and titles and give students guidance about the fieldwork investigation. However, if you are completing an individual investigation (choosing your own task statement and title) check with your teacher that your choice of task and title are appropriate.

> **Task marking** is called 'medium control' because both the school and the Examination Board are involved (i.e. the Examination Board does not have total control).

© Pearson Education Ltd, 2010

What does Controlled Assessment test?

Controlled Assessment tests the following two areas:
- the application of knowledge and understanding
- the use of geographical skills and techniques.

What does this mean?

Testing the 'application of knowledge and understanding' means:
- assessing the level of background knowledge you show about the topic being investigated and how well you show that you understand the topic
- assessing how well you show that you understand the importance of using information (data)
- assessing how well you show that you understand that information is not always reliable or detailed enough to draw effective conclusions.

Testing the 'use of geographical skills and techniques' means:
- assessing how well you identified the information needed to complete your investigation
- assessing how effective you were at collecting information from a number of different sources
- assessing how well you presented information through the use of a variety of techniques, including ICT
- assessing how well you used your collected information to reach a conclusion.

What are the advantages of Controlled Assessment?

Although completing a geographical investigation can be quite challenging, it has many advantages, some of which are shown below.

It is a part of your Geography GCSE that you have some control over.

It is worth 25 per cent of your GCSE, so could make a big difference to your final grade.

It is a good way to develop your understanding of a particular part of your GCSE course.

The Controlled Assessment topic might also come up in the final exams.

It gives you an opportunity to look in more detail at a topic you have enjoyed in class.

Safety First!

Completing a geographical investigation involves collecting information outside of school, so always:
- listen to advice about safety
- discuss any individual data collection plans with teachers and parents
- do not go to places alone
- keep people informed about what you are doing.

© Pearson Education Ltd, 2010

How will your fieldwork investigation be marked?

Your fieldwork investigation will be marked using an official mark scheme produced by the Examination Board (AQA). The mark scheme identifies five areas of assessment (called the marking criteria).

The table below lists the five marking criteria and explains briefly what you need to do in order to satisfy them.

Marking criteria	Criteria checklist – The following questions highlight what you need to do.	
Geographical understanding	• Is the location of your investigation clearly identified?	
	• Have you identified the key ideas or terms that are important to your investigation?	
	• Have you linked the key ideas to the data collection methods?	
	• Have you returned to the key ideas in your interpretation, conclusion and evaluation?	
Methodology	• Have you stated the aim of your investigation and decribed the sequence of investigation?	
	• Have you included primary data?	
	• Have you described, explained and justified your data collection methods?	
	• Have you included at least one set of original data?	
	• Is your completed work well organised?	
Presentation	• Has ICT (information and communications technology) been used to present some or all of your data?	
	• Have you used a number of different presentation methods?	
	• Have you included more complex presentation methods?	
	• Are your presentation methods accurate and complete?	
Interpretation and QWC (Quality of Written Communication)	• Have you described, explained and analysed the main points from your data collection?	
	• Have you identified and explained any links between your data?	
	• Have you returned to the original key ideas expressed in your introduction?	
	• Have you included a conclusion which is clearly linked to the original aim of the investigation?	
	• Is spelling, punctuation and grammer of a high standard?	
Evaluation	• Have you mentioned how well your data collection methods worked?	
	• Have you suggested how your data collection methods might be improved?	
	• Have you considered what other data might have been useful?	
	• Have you considered the extent to which your data collection methods provided you with accurate information?	
	• Have you considered how limitations of data collection methods and problems of accuracy may have affected your conclusions?	

Good Idea As you work through your investigation, use the marking criteria checklist above to identify the strengths and weaknesses of your work by placing ticks or crosses next to each point in this column.

© Pearson Education Ltd, 2010

How is the mark decided for each of the marking criteria?

1. Each of the five marking criteria is worth up to twelve marks.

2. Each of the marking criteria is divided into three levels, with each level having four marks. For example:

Level 1 is worth 1 to 4 marks   Lowest level

Level 2 is worth 5 to 8 marks

Level 3 is worth 9 to 12 marks   Highest level

3. The Examination Board produces a detailed mark scheme which describes what is required to achieve the mark in each level.

What does the mark scheme look like?

The table below shows a simplified version of the mark scheme.

The complete, official mark scheme can be found on the AQA website (www.aqa.org.uk).

Simplified mark scheme

Marking criteria	Level 1 (1–4 marks)	Level 2 (5–8 marks) Requirements of Level 1 fulfilled and;	Level 3 (9–12 marks) Requirements of Level 2 fulfilled and;
Geographical understanding	• A basic description of the location of the investigation. • The key ideas about the topic being investigated are identified and described.	• Investigation clearly located. • The key ideas about the topic are clearly applied to the investigation through the data collection methods. • Returns to the key ideas within the interpretation.	• Detailed locational understanding. • Returns to the key ideas and applies them to the interpretation, conclusion and evaluation.
Methodology	• Identifies a topic for investigation. • Describes the background to the investigation. • Lists methods of data collection.	• Describes the sequence of the investigation. • Clear evidence of primary data collection. • Report is planned and well organised.	• Data collection methods are described and explained. • Clear evidence of individual data collection which is relevant to the investigation.
Presentation	• Limited range of basic presentation techniques. • At least one example of ICT use.	• Good range of appropriate presentation techniques accurately used.	• Wide range of appropriate and accurate presentation techniques. • At least two more complex presentation techniques. • Uses ICT to present most of the information.
Interpretation and QWC (Quality of Written Communication)	• Brief discussion of results with simple reasons for them. • Written work is legible with reasonable accuracy of spelling, punctuation and grammar.	• Description and explanation of results with valid reasoning. • Simple conclusions related to the original idea. • Some use of geographical language. • Considerable accuracy of spelling, punctuation and grammar.	• Describes, explains and analyses results in detail, with clear links to original idea. • Identifies links between data. • Detailed conclusion linked to original aim of investigation. • Considerable accuracy of spelling, punctuation and grammar.
Evaluation	• Considers the effectiveness of data collection methods. • Suggests how data collection methods might have been improved.	• Identifies specific problems of data collection and considers how this might have affected accuracy of results. • Suggests how improvements to data collection may improve levels of accuracy.	• Considers how issues relating to data collection methods and accuracy of results might affect conclusions. • Shows an understanding of the connections between methods, results and conclusions.

© Pearson Education Ltd, 2010

OVER TO YOU

Use the simplified mark scheme:

- to identify exactly what is required before you start writing your report
- to identify any areas that you need to develop in order to achieve at the highest level
- as a final checklist before you give your report in.

Notes

© Pearson Education Ltd, 2010

Understanding the mark scheme

It is important to understand how the mark scheme works. There are a number of points within each of the marking criteria that you should remember if you want to reach the highest levels. Some of these are outlined on these two pages.

Geographical understanding

Locating your investigation

- The location of your study can be described using words, but this is often self-limiting and may restrict you to level 1 marks.
- Using a map to show the general location and a more detailed, annotated map to show the specific study area is often a more successful way of clearly locating an investigation. It also gives opportunities to use presentation techniques (see pages 66–67).

Caution!

Simply downloading a map and marking the study area with an arrow will not always say much about the location. Removing information that is not important to the investigation and adding relevant annotations might help to show the study area more clearly (see page 67).

Methodology

Remember!

- This piece of work is called a **local fieldwork investigation**, so it **must** contain primary data. If there is no primary data you will not get beyond Level 1 on this section.
- In order to reach Level 3 your investigation **must** include at least one data collection method which is individual to you. Make sure you explain how your individual data collection method(s) made a significant contribution to your investigation.

Caution!

- Unique or individual data collection must 'make a clear contribution to your investigation' so must not be things like:
  - an extra question on a questionnaire
  - one extra two minute traffic count
  - an isolated photograph put on the front cover.
- It is not always easy to identify individuality when extra work has been carried out by a group of students. Where this is the case, each individual must show that they have made a clear contribution to the extra work.

Good Advice

Use the 'collecting and presenting information' section (pages 17–57) to identify possible data collection methods that you might use.

OVER TO YOU

Make a brief note of:

1   Where you might find appropriate location maps.

2   Any 'individual' data that might be appropriate to your investigation.

© Pearson Education Ltd, 2010

Presentation

You need to use a range of appropriate presentation techniques to present your data. Use the 'collecting and presenting information' section (pages 17–57) to identify useful data presentation methods.

Use of more complex methods

In order to reach Level 3 you have to use 'at least two more complex presentation skills'. These do not have to be completed using ICT if you have already met the ICT requirements.

More complex presentation skills might include:

- Choropleth maps
- Isoline maps
- Proportional symbol maps
- Proportional flow line maps
- Annotated cross-sections/profiles
- Photographs / field sketches with detailed annotations
- Accurate scattergraphs (with best fit lines)
- Statistical techniques (where all the working is shown)

Good Advice

You will only get marks for presentation skills if they are accurate and complete. Using more complex presentation skills that are inaccurate or incomplete will not allow you to reach Level 3!

Caution!

Use of ICT

- If there is no use of ICT you will not earn any marks at all from this part of the marking criteria no matter how good your presentation might be.
- A single use of ICT to present information is needed to access Level 1 marks.
- Word processing does not meet the ICT requirements – you have to use ICT methods to present information, for example; graphs, maps, tables of figures, flow diagrams, digital photographs.

OVER TO YOU

Use the 'collecting and presenting information' section and textbooks to identify possible data presentation methods that you might use.

Notes

_____

_____

_____

_____

_____

_____

_____

_____

_____

_____

_____

_____

_____

_____

_____

_____

_____

_____

_____

© Pearson Education Ltd, 2010

Interpretation (and QWC)

Interpretation means

Describing data	→	Explaining and analysing data	→	Identifying links between data

What is QWC?

QWC stands for Quality of Written Communication. This is about the general quality of your communication skills (spelling, punctuation and grammar). Always check this carefully when you have completed your investigation.

Evaluation

This is really asking you to reflect on your work and assess the value of your investigation. It is not about making simple statements such as, 'Everything went really well' or 'I had problems because it rained', without any explanation!

The key to a good evaluation is to consider:

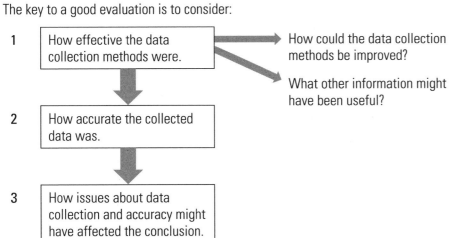

1   How effective the data collection methods were.

     How could the data collection methods be improved?

     What other information might have been useful?

2   How accurate the collected data was.

3   How issues about data collection and accuracy might have affected the conclusion.

What is meant by Analyse?

Analyse means more than just explaining the data. It means breaking the data down and picking out the most important parts in relation to the title of your fieldwork investigation.

OVER TO YOU

Make a note of any problems or limitations of your data collection methods as you go. (Refer back to it when you write up your evaluation).

Notes

_____
_____
_____
_____
_____
_____
_____
_____
_____
_____
_____
_____
_____
_____
_____
_____
_____

© Pearson Education Ltd, 2010

Section 2: Getting started

Thinking about your investigation

Having chosen, or been given, a question or hypothesis for your investigation, you will then need to make a start. It is often useful to spend some time thinking about a number of general questions, which are important to all investigations and then put together a plan of action. This should include a list of things to be done, with a clear idea about how much time should be spent on each task.

General questions

1 **What is the title of your fieldwork investigation?** The title is the first thing the examiner sees, so it needs to say exactly what the investigation is about. It is often helpful to include some locational or place context in the title. For example:

    'How important is tourism to the local economy in Bakewell?'

    'What pressures do increasing visitor numbers create in the honeypot town of Castleton?'

2 **Where is the area of study?** Is your fieldwork investigation about a particular place, a part of a town or a general area? Identify the specific area you are investigating by looking at Ordnance Survey maps or town plans.

3 **What are the key ideas and words associated with your fieldwork investigation?** It is useful to write down all the ideas and words you can think of that are linked to your investigation. For example, if you are carrying out a shopping investigation, the following ideas and words might provide a helpful starting point:

IDEAS
- People travel further to shop in larger shopping centres.
- Larger towns have more shops and services.
- People don't travel far for day-to-day goods.
- Central business districts contain national stores.
- Central shopping areas are often pedestrianised.

THINK

WORDS
Shops/services
Sphere of influence
Shopping hierarchy
Frequency of visit
Comparison goods
Convenience goods
Threshold population
Low/high order goods
Pedestrianisation
National chain stores

4 **Where can you find background information for your fieldwork investigation?** Use textbooks, local newspapers, websites and any local information to identify important points, and add any new ideas to your original list.

© Pearson Education Ltd, 2010

OVER TO YOU

Title of investigation

General Questions

1 What is the extent of the area you need to identify for your investigation? (i.e., if your investigation is about a town centre, do you need a map of the whole town?)

_____

_____

_____

1 What are the key ideas and words that come in to your mind when you think about the title of your investigation?

Ideas	Words

You can add to, or modify the points mentioned here as you continue to work on your investigation.

© Pearson Education Ltd, 2010

Plan of action

The following plan will help you to understand the overall organisational framework for your fieldwork investigation.

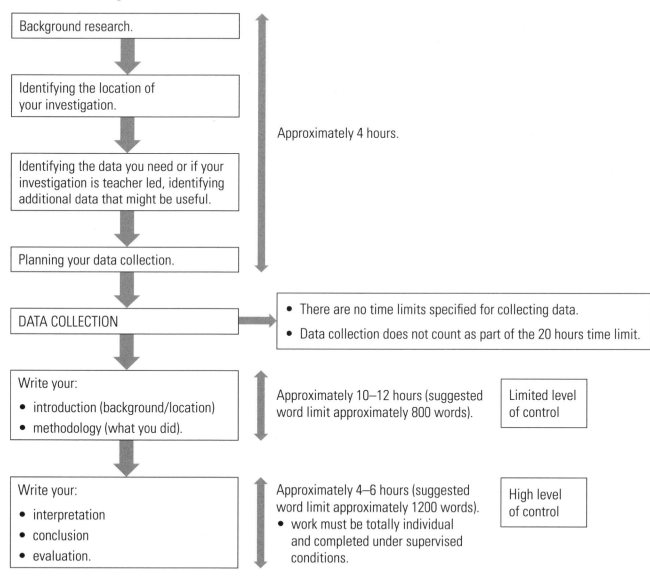

Background research.	
Identifying the location of your investigation.	Approximately 4 hours.
Identifying the data you need or if your investigation is teacher led, identifying additional data that might be useful.	
Planning your data collection.	
DATA COLLECTION	• There are no time limits specified for collecting data. • Data collection does not count as part of the 20 hours time limit.
Write your: • introduction (background/location) • methodology (what you did).	Approximately 10–12 hours (suggested word limit approximately 800 words). — Limited level of control
Write your: • interpretation • conclusion • evaluation.	Approximately 4–6 hours (suggested word limit approximately 1200 words). • work must be totally individual and completed under supervised conditions. — High level of control

Remember!

- There is a maximum time limit of **20 hours** (excluding time spent on data collection) for the completion of the whole Controlled Assessment task.

- There is a word guidance of 2000 words.

The timings suggested here are flexible **but** the total should not exceed 20 hours.

© Pearson Education Ltd, 2010

Background research

Background research is the first stage of any investigation. It is important because it will:

- *Provide valuable background information about the topic* – You might not end up using all of the information, but it will help you to understand the context of your investigation (what it is about). It may also help you to decide what information is important for your investigation.

- *Identify any links there may be to geographical theory* – Some investigations are about comparing theory (what is expected) to an actual local example. To do this you need a good understanding about the original theory.

- *Help you to identify any useful key words and definitions* – Using geographical words and definitions is a good way of identifying important ideas and showing understanding about the topic you are investigating.

AQA Guidance

- You will be able to research your task by using your class notes, books, the school library and any other resources you have at school, including the internet.

- You will be able to have access to your research notes when writing up the investigation.

The following examples show a range of research notes that could be made for a river investigation. Remember however, that this is a small-scale investigation and the word limit is only 2000 words.

Task Option - *Investigate how features of a river change over distance*

Title of investigation - *How do the characteristics of the River Burr change from its source to Burrbridge?*

Basic river words/definitions that might be useful

Source - *where a river / stream begins*

Tributary - *a smaller stream flowing into a larger stream*

Confluence - *where streams / rivers join*

Valley - *a depression usually occupied by a stream (shape of a valley may change downstream)*

Long profile - *section of a river from the source* $\longrightarrow$ *downstream*

(Could use an OS map to draw this?)

Cross profile - *section across the river (a number of cross-sections along the river might be useful)*

Good Ideas

- Keep all of your background information in a research file.

- Be aware of any health and safety issues — you might mention them in your methodology and evaluation.

- Make sure that you make a note of the sources of any information (including websites) because:

  - you may need to find the sources again

  - you should include the sources of all information you have used in your bibliography.

Safety Notes

- In this area the river is quite narrow and shallow.

- The approximate length of this section of the river is 4km – it is very accessible.

Must consider

Risk assessment / safety!

© Pearson Education Ltd, 2010

The main river processes

Erosion - *wearing away of rocks*

Types of erosion:

Hydraulic action - *force of water*

Abrasion - *material carried by river acting like sandpaper*

Attrition - *material carried by river acting like sandpaper*

Solution - *rocks dissolved by water*

Bedload - *material being carried by the river (could measure the type of bedload at different places – size of pebbles, roundness etc.)*

Movement of material

Traction - *rolling along river bed*

Saltation - *pebbles bouncing along river bed*

Suspension - *fine material (mud / silt) being carried by river*

Solution - *material dissolved in the water*

Vertical *erosion – downwards*

Lateral *erosion – sideways*

Measuring the river

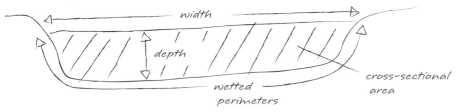

- measuring cross-sectional area *(approximately) – width x depth*
- measuring efficiency of river *(called hydraulic radius)* *hydraulic radius* = $\dfrac{\text{cross-sectional area}}{\text{wetted perimeter}}$

    (higher number = more efficient)
- measuring the speed of the river - *time a float over a specific distance*

What are the key ideas for the investigation?

1 *How does the river valley change downstream?*

2 *How does the river change downstream?*

3 *Are there any specific features?*

4 *Does the bedload change downstream?*

5 *Does the river become more efficient as it flows downstream?*

Main feature of the River Burr is a meander (bend in the river)

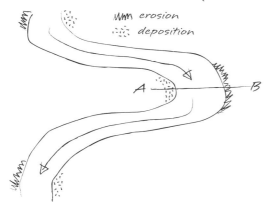

Cross-section

© Pearson Education Ltd, 2010

Your background research

Use the following two pages to identify relevant background information for your fieldwork investigation. This could be the starting point for your 'research file'.

OVER TO YOU	
Task Option	
Title of investigation	
Research notes	**Source of information**

© Pearson Education Ltd, 2010

Research notes	Source of information

© Pearson Education Ltd, 2010

Section 3: Collecting and presenting information

Introduction to data gathering

Gathering the information you need for your investigation is probably the most important part of the whole process. Without a good range of information (data) it will be difficult for your work to score high marks. The diagram below explains why.

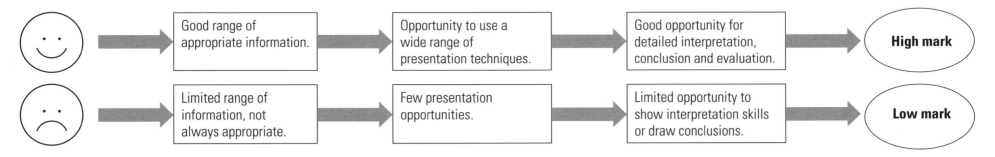

Primary and secondary data

There are two main types of information (usually called data). These are shown in the table below.

Type of data	Definition	Examples
Primary data	Original information collected first-hand by fieldwork.	Measuring Counting Assessing Interviewing Sketch mapping Taking photographs
Secondary data	Information from published sources which was collected by someone else.	Census data Textbooks Planning documents Local newspapers Leaflets Maps Directories Websites Photographs

Good Advice

The most successful investigations use secondary data to show a general understanding of the topic and primary data to link it to the local area.

Don't Forget!

Use of technology.

There are a number of ways that information can be collected using newer technology, including:
- Google Earth
- Geographical Positioning Systems (GPS)
- Camera phones
- Automatic counting / measuring devices

Using this section to develop your investigation

Remember!

Task options are provided by AQA (Examples for 2011 are shown on page 7).
Your investigation must clearly fit the chosen task option.

The task statements are often quite general, so the actual title of your investigation does not have to be exactly the same as the task option provided by AQA. However, your investigation must clearly fit in with the key idea expressed in the task option.

For example, if your investigation is taken from the tourism part of the specification, the task statement set for 2011 is:

'Investigate a UK National Park or coastal resort as a tourist destination.'

From this general task option it would be possible to consider a number of different investigations, for example:

'How important is tourism to the local economy of ....?'

'An assessment of the number and type of visitors to ....'

'Is seasonality a problem in ....?'

'To what extent is .... dominated by tourism?'

'What issues are created by a large number of visitors to ....?'

'How effective is visitor management in the tourist honeypot of ....?'

Types of investigations

Controlled Assessment investigations are usually one of the following:

- Teacher guided investigations – where students are given a question, or hypothesis, and data collection is organised by the teacher, often through a local fieldwork day.
- Individual investigations – where students develop their own question, or hypothesis, using the task options and statements provided by AQA and then collect individual data.

If you are carrying out an individual investigation make sure that:

- the topic is clearly related to the task statement provided
- you have easy and safe access to the study area
- the investigation is not too large and can be completed within the prescribed time period
- the topic allows you to score marks in all levels of the marking criteria.

Key Point

Your assessment is called a local fieldwork investigation so it should:

- be small in scale
- give the opportunity for primary data collection.

For example:

An investigation which considers the importance of tourism to the local economy within a national park might:

- briefly consider the whole of the national park using secondary data and
- focus on one small town or area within the national park by using primary evidence.

Remember!

- You are producing a fieldwork report not a book!
- Your final report should not be more than 2000 words in length.

What is a hypothesis?

A hypothesis is a brief statement that can be proved or disproved. For example, a hypothesis might be 'Most people who shop in Guildford live within a twenty mile radius'. Data is then collected in order to prove or disprove this statement.

© Pearson Education Ltd, 2010

Teacher-guided investigations

If you are completing a teacher-guided investigation use this section to:

- help you explain why your data collection methods are important to your investigation
- help you to identify at least one individual data collection method that you might use
- identify data presentation methods that you could use.

Individual investigation

If you are completing an individual investigation use this section to:

1. identify data collection methods that would be relevant to your investigation
2. help you explain why your chosen data collection methods are important to your investigation
3. identify the data presentation methods that you could use

Where should you start?

In order to get the highest marks for your data collection, the data **must** be linked to your investigation title and not simply collected for the sake of it. Ask yourself the following two questions:

1   What information do I need to address my title?
2   Why is this information important to my investigation?

Start with a 'thinking exercise' like the one below. This will help you identify the types of data that might be useful for your investigation.

Title of investigation: Should St James's Street be pedestrianised?	
What information might be useful?	Why might the information be useful?
Traffic flow data	To see how busy St James's Street is. If St James' Street is pedestrianised, the traffic will have to use other roads.
Land-use survey	To see if the area is part of the Central Business District, an area which is pedestrianised in many town centres.
Pedestrian count	To see how many people use the area.
Questionnaire	To get people's views about traffic problems and pedestrianisation in the area.

© Pearson Education Ltd, 2010

Don't Forget!

There are extra marks for individuality. Use this section to identify one or two extra individual data sources that might be appropriate to your investigation.

Remember!

Your Controlled Assessment is called a **local fieldwork investigation** so it **must** include primary data!

Good Idea

When collecting primary data always make a note of when, how and where it was collected. Also make a note of any problems that you may have had, and think of any limitations to the data collection method.

OVER TO YOU

Title of investigation ....

Look through the whole of this section carefully.

1 Identify any data collection methods that might be useful to your investigation.

Data collection method	Page	Why it might be useful

2 Identify any data presentation method that might be useful to your investigation.

Data presentation method	Page	Data to be presented

© Pearson Education Ltd, 2010

Locating your investigation

It is important that you show:

- the general location of your investigation (where it is in relation to the surroundings)
- the actual site of your investigation (where you carried out your data collection).

The best way of showing the location and site of your investigation is by using maps.

Using Ordnance Survey (OS) maps

Ordnance Survey (OS) maps are available at different scales and can be used to:

- locate the general area of your investigation and to prepare a detailed base map
- give you useful background information about the area under investigation.

The most useful types of OS maps available are shown in the table below.

Type of map	Scale	General description
Superplan	1:2500	Very detailed map with individual houses, shops and industries shown. Useful to show the specific area of your investigation.
Land plan	1:10000	Shows general land use and identifies rural/urban differences.
Explorer	1:25000	Shows general urban/rural patterns and detailed physical features.
Landranger	1:50000	Covers a large area and shows general patterns. Useful to show the general location of your investigation.

OVER TO YOU

Title of investigation ....

Use this space to make a note of the source of maps that could be used to:

- locate your study area
- provide a detailed plan of your study area.

Good Advice

Local maps are available from a number of places, including:

- planning offices
- tourist information offices
- newspaper offices
- estate agents.

© Pearson Education Ltd, 2010

Using written information

Written information can come from a variety of sources, including:

- local newspaper articles
- business magazines
- Tourist Board information brochures
- local authority departments
- Environmental Management organisations (National Parks, English Nature, National Trust etc.)
- specific environmental management areas (nature reserves, river parks etc.)
- government departments such as the Environment Agency.

How can written information be useful?

Written information is a very useful source of secondary data. It can be used in a number of ways, including:

- helping to locate your investigation
- helping to set the scene and give background information about the topic you are investigating
- providing facts and figures
- highlighting issues and conflicts
- identifying different opinions about a particular issue
- helping to describe and explain any existing management strategies that are linked to your investigation topic.

How should you use articles?

Any written articles you find will not have been written specifically for your investigation! Consequently, it is important to identify the information that is relevant to your investigation.

The following examples show two ways that written articles can be used in your investigation.

1   Identifying the key points and making recorded notes in a table like the one shown below.

What the article is about	Important points	Source
Pessures on National Parks as a result of increasing visitor numbers	• the issue of second home ownership • problems of footpath erosion • local shops being taken over by cafes and souvenir shops • parking and traffic issues	Yorkshire Star newspaper (16.2.2010)

> **Think!**
>
> Most government and private organisations have websites, which might have useful information.

© Pearson Education Ltd, 2010

2 Include the complete article and highlight the key points. The following example shows articles used in an investigation about visitor pressure in the Peak District National Park.

Headline expresses the pressure on the Peak District National Park.

Loved to death

The Peak District National Park opened on April 17, 1951, and was rapidly followed by nine other parks. National parks are not just about environmentalism. They are pivotal in rural economies. On top of the annual government funding of around £26 million and the same again from EU and other sources, they attract 100 million visitors a year.

The Peak District park, for example, is the most visited park in the world after Mount Fuji in Japan. Each year its 550 square miles receive more than 30 million visitors.

The pressures from vehicles and walkers intensify constantly, and the park is often close to breaking-point. On Sundays and bank holidays, traffic can be gridlocked around Longdendale.

Solving the traffic problems will not cure another great concern - erosion of paths by millions of walkers. When one stretch of the Pennine Way opened it was "a wee sheep track" but it grew to 60 metres in width. Now footpath teams work constantly to stabilise erosion.

With the increase in visitor numbers there is increasing demand for new roads and the building of hotels.

© adapted from Carolyn Murrow-Brown, *The Times*, 14 April 2001.

Suggests an environment / economic conflict.

Large number of visitors.

Identifies key pressures.

Suggests weekend / seasonal pressures (honeypots?).

Footpath erosion seen as a major problem.

Increasing pressure linked to building.

Keep off the grass!

With growing popularity there is increasing concern about traffic and associated pollution in National Parks. However, in recent years the growth in popularity of mountain biking and four wheel drive vehicles in the Peak District National Park has added another pressure to the environment. The use of motor vehicles on tracks can create massive damage, especially after heavy rainfall. There is also concern that plant and animal life could be affected by the noise and pollution of motor vehicles.

A local farmer said that "the use of recreational vehicles on dirt tracks can cause massive gulleys. One vehicle can cause the damage of 500 pairs of feet."

Concerns about local ecosystems.

May express a local conflict.

Links to natural conditions (rainfall).

OVER TO YOU

Use this table to list any secondary information sources you use.

Source of information	Important points
	• • •
	• • •
	• • •

© Pearson Education Ltd, 2010

Using census information

What is a census?

A census is a population survey. In the United Kingdom a census is carried out every ten years, on the first year of each new decade: i.e. 1971, 1981, 1991, 2001, 2011 etc.

The UK National Census provides information at a range of scales, from neighbourhood areas containing a small number of people right up to national information about the whole country. The most useful scale for local investigations is either neighbourhood or ward information. (A ward is an area which usually contains over 2000 people.)

However, comparing local area data with the national average can be very useful in some investigations. Census data is also very useful for identifying change over time.

What is included in the National Census?

The National Census collects information about a range of socio-economic characteristics, including:

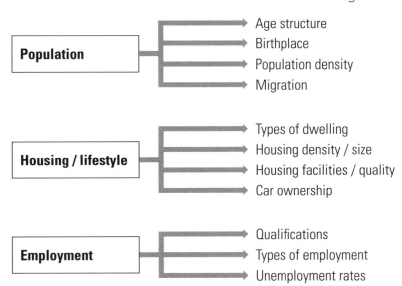

Population
→ Age structure
→ Birthplace
→ Population density
→ Migration

Housing / lifestyle
→ Types of dwelling
→ Housing density / size
→ Housing facilities / quality
→ Car ownership

Employment
→ Qualifications
→ Types of employment
→ Unemployment rates

Find out more:

Information about the UK Census is held at the Office for National Statistics.

www.ons.gov.uk/census

The National Census website also lists lots of other sources of information which might be useful.

Good Idea

Although the National Census is only carried out every ten years, local authorities collect information all the time. You can get a lot of background data, maps, photographs etc. via your local authority website. Each local authority has a number of departments, including planning, housing, transport, environment etc. Would information from any of the local authority departments in your area be useful for your investigation?

Other sources of useful information:

- The Index of Multiple Deprivation (IMD) uses seven sets of data to work out how deprived (poor) areas are. This can be used to compare different parts of urban areas or different rural settlements. Find out more at: www.communities.gov.uk
- Educational attainment information can be found at: DCSF (www.dcsf.gov.uk)
- Health information can be found at: Department of Health (www.dh.gov.uk).

© Pearson Education Ltd, 2010

How might you use census data?

The following examples suggest how census information is often a very useful source of secondary data to some investigations.

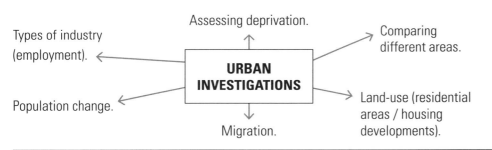

Remember!

Population change creates the need for other changes and can put added pressure on areas. For example:

Increasing number of people ⟹ more cars ⟹ increasing traffic problems.

Consequently population data can be useful in a variety of human investigations.

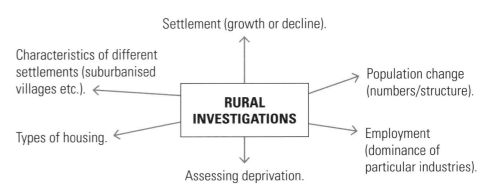

OVER TO YOU

Title of investigation

Look at the sources / types of data mentioned on these two pages. Identify any information that might be useful to your investigation. Make a note of the source and type of information. Briefly explain how it might be useful to your investigation.	**Source of information:** Why it might be useful?
	Source of information: Why it might be useful?

© Pearson Education Ltd, 2010

Presenting census information

The following examples show some of the information that can be found in the National Census and different ways that it can be presented.

Line graph

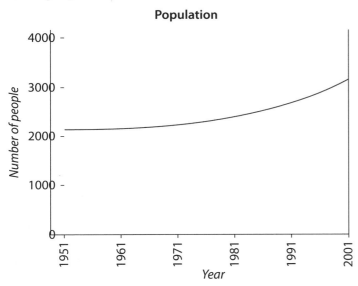

Population

Multiple line graph

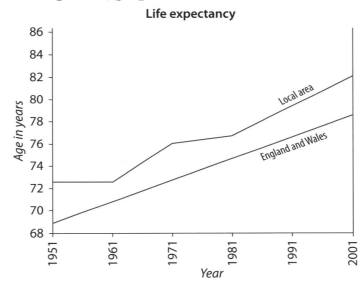

Life expectancy

Bar graph

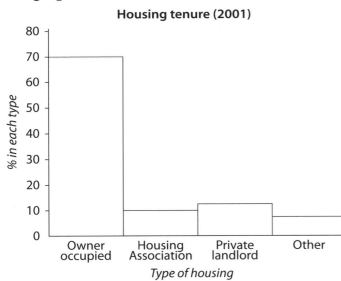

Housing tenure (2001)

Multiple bar graph

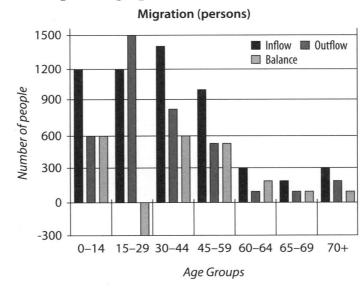

Migration (persons)

Good Idea

Multiple line and bar graphs are a useful technique for comparing information.

Pie chart

Housing type

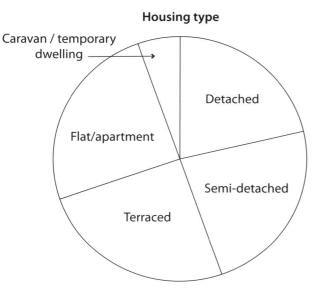

Caravan / temporary dwelling

Detached

Flat/apartment

Semi-detached

Terraced

Divided bar graph

Housing type

Caravan / temporary dwelling

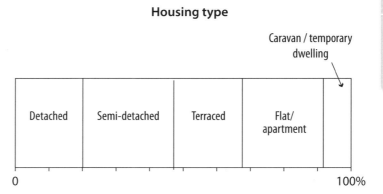

| Detached | Semi-detached | Terraced | Flat/apartment | |

0   100%

Think!

The presentation techniques on these two pages could also be used to present other information — for example, questionnaire data.

Choropleth map

A choropleth, or shading, map can be used to show patterns within an area.

- The information being mapped needs to be divided into groups (classes). Four or five groups are usually needed to show a clear pattern without the map becoming too complicated.
- A colour or type of shading is used for each class, making sure the shading becomes darker for the higher values.

Population density

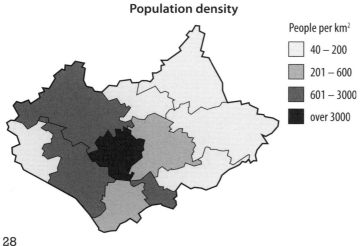

People per km²

☐	40 – 200
▨	201 – 600
▨	601 – 3000
■	over 3000

Table of figures

Employment (%)	
Agriculture / forestry	2.8
Fishing	1.4
Quarrying/mining	2.7
Manufacturing	14.2
Construction	6.8
Retail	18.3
Transport	6.5
Hotel / catering	16.3
Property management	7.8
Health / education / social services	23.2

Good Idea

There may be different methods of presenting the same information. Use the method that shows the information most clearly – it will be easier to interpret!

Good Idea

Remember to use a range of presentation techniques in your investigation.

© Pearson Education Ltd, 2010

Using questionnaires

Questionnaires are an excellent source of primary data and can be used to collect information about:

- people's habits
- people's views and opinions.

Constructing a questionnaire

A questionnaire must be carefully planned if it is going to provide useful data. It is not just about asking questions, it is about asking **appropriate** questions!

In order to produce an effective questionnaire you need to consider the following factors:

- What information will be useful to your investigation?
- How does each of the questions relate to your investigation?

What types of information can you obtain from respondents? (people who answer questionnaires)

- Background data about the respondents, for example:
  - age and gender information
  - occupational data.
- Activity data, for example:
  - how often people go shopping
  - how often people visit a park
  - what local facilities people use.
- Attitude data (what people think), for example:
  - Do you think a new road should be built?
  - What do you think about the environmental or shopping quality of an area?
  - Do you think a particular place needs more facilities?

Trying out your questionnaire

It is always a good idea to test or 'pilot' your questionnaire by trying it out on a small number of people. You can then adjust any questions that do not seem to work.

How many people should you ask?

You are going to draw conclusions from the results of your questionnaire, so you need to get enough evidence to be sure that your results are a true representation of the general population (a 'representative sample'). For a shopping survey this might mean between 50 and 100 people; for a small village study, 10 to 20 people might be a reasonable representative sample. The number of people you ask might also be determined by the type of questions. If your questionnaire has only short questions, you could ask a larger number of people.

Good Advice

- Teacher guided investigations often use questionnaires as a common source of data.

  However, if it is appropriate, you could carry out a second questionnaire, which is focused on a particular target audience you have identified as important to your investigation.

- Questionnaires are most frequently used in human geography investigations.

  However, it might be appropriate to use a questionnaire in a mainly physical geography investigation. For example, when considering the recreational use or management of a river or coastal area.

- Remember to consider the length of your questionnaire. If there are too many questions the impact on the 2000 word limit is greater, so keep it relevant.

Remember!

Questions can give **objective information** (facts) and **subjective information** (opinions).

Good Idea

Use a round number of questionnaires (10, 20, 50, 100 etc.). This will make it easier for you to work out percentages and pie charts.

How do you select the people to ask?

Selecting people to answer a questionnaire is called sampling. You cannot ask everybody, so you need to select or sample a number of people.

- The type of people you ask must reflect the aim of your investigation. For example, in a study about car parking problems asking non-drivers, or very young people, will be of limited use.
- If your investigation affects the whole community, but you only question young people, you will not get a very representative sample.

There are three main types of sampling:

- **Random sampling** – where each member of a population has an equal chance of being selected. For example, in a street questionnaire every house number is put in a bag and ten are selected at random.
- **Stratified sampling** – where the proportion of respondents is selected according to the topic. For example, in a questionnaire about youth club facilities it might make more sense to ask a larger proportion of younger people.
- **Systematic sampling** – where a regular sample is taken. For example, every tenth person, every fifth house, every ten metres.

How can you get personal data?

- When asking questions make a note of the sex and approximate age of the respondents (young / middle aged / older).
- Make questions less personal by offering a broad choice of options. For example:

'How old are you?' (Tick one box.) | 15 – 25 | | 26 – 40 | | 41 – 55 | | 56 – 65 | | Over 65 |

Types of questions

The types of question you ask will be determined by whether you need lots of simple information or a limited amount of more detailed information. The two main types of question are:

Closed questions

Short-answer questions, often with a yes / no tick box response. This type of question is an excellent way of collecting lots of information very quickly but do not always give detailed responses.

Open questions

Questions where respondents can make longer, general comments. This type of question can provide considerable detail but can take a long time, and answers may be more subjective (opinions).

How long should a questionnaire be?

The length of a questionnaire will depend upon what you are trying to find out, but usually a questionnaire should not have more than ten questions. Questionnaires with mainly open questions should have fewer questions.

Good Idea

When you write up your methodology explain:

- how you piloted your questionnaire
- how you decided the number and type of people to ask.

Safety First

When planning questionnaires **always** make sure your parents and teachers know what you are doing, and **always** work in pairs.

© Pearson Education Ltd, 2010

How should you lay out a questionnaire?

The most successful questionnaires usually start with several closed questions, which gather general information and end with a limited number of open questions.

OVER TO YOU

Title of investigation ....

If a questionnaire (or an additional questionnaire) is a useful source of data for your investigation:

1 List the types of information you would like to find out from your questionnaire.

2 Think about the number and type of people you might ask.

3 'Rough out' a number of questions that might help you get the information you would like.

Remember!

Your report should only be 2000 words in length so you should only use a small number of really important questions.

Presenting questionnaire data

The methods you choose to present your questionnaire data will be determined by the types of questions you have asked.
The following techniques are frequently used to present information obtained from questionnaires:

- bar graphs (page 27)
- pie charts (page 28)
- tables of figures
- pictograms
- desire line maps.

Pictograms

Pictograms are picture graphs where the picture gives a visual representation of the data. For example:

Question: How did you travel here today?

Each complete symbol represents 5 people

Desire line map

A desire line map is drawn to show the movement of people, either individually or in groups.
For example, in a shopping centre investigation:

Question: Which town / village did you come from today?

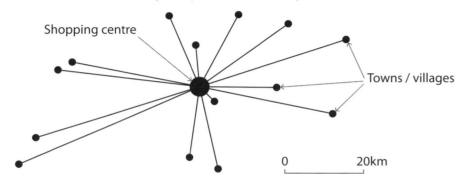

Place names could be added if it is important.

© Pearson Education Ltd, 2010

Using interviews

Interviews are a useful source of primary data. They can give you a lot of detailed and well informed information and can be more objective than a questionnaire.

Preparing for an interview

1   Think about the types of interviewees who could provide helpful information for your investigation.

For example:

It might be helpful to interview:

Task option - TOURISM

Task statement: Investigate a UK National Park or coastal resort as a tourist destination.

- Local tourist office manager
- Hotel owner
- National Park ranger
- Local authority employees

2   **(a)** Work out exactly what you need to find out, e.g. in the above example you might ask the National Park ranger about the environmental pressures that large numbers of visitors bring to National Parks.

   (b) Prepare a number of key questions that will help you to focus on the information you need.

3   Think about any additional secondary data that the interviewee might have that could be useful to your investigation.

4   Always remember that interviewees are helping you and giving up their time, so:
   - create a good impression by being well presented, polite and well prepared
   - be punctual and well organised and don't take too long.

Presenting interview information

A ten-minute interview may run into hundreds of words! When you go back over an interview the key is to identify the most important points. (Those that are closely linked to the title of your investigation.) These points need to be highlighted when you present your interview data.

How can the key points be presented?

There are a number of ways that interview data can be presented, including:
- a simple list of the most important points
- a list of the key points mentioned by each interviewee (important when there are different opinions about something)
- using speech bubbles and writing a brief statement identifying the key points mentioned by each interviewee.

Good Idea

A lot of teacher guided investigations use a common questionnaire. Interviews can be used to support questionnaire data or get extra information. This could be evidence of individual data collection.

Good Ideas

- If you are not sure about your questions try them out on a friend first. If they are not clear or appear to be too personal make adjustments to them.
- You could tape interviews but always ask the interviewee if they mind!

Safety First

- Discuss any individual interviews you may be thinking of doing with your teacher or parents.
- Work in pairs – one person asking questions while the other takes notes.

© Pearson Education Ltd, 2010

Using speech bubbles to present interview information

National Park ranger

Hotel manager

Tourist Office manager

The advantage of this type of presentation is that it clearly identifies the views of different people and is a visual presentation. However, you must make sure that the statements in each speech bubble are an accurate representation of the points made by the interviewee!

OVER TO YOU

Title of investigation

List three different people who might be able to provide useful information for your investigation.	What questions might you ask each of the three people?
•	•
•	•
•	•

© Pearson Education Ltd, 2010

Using simple scoring surveys

A simple, graded, scoring survey is a good way of gathering information and can be used in a variety of investigations.

Basic number / description grids, like those shown below, will often give a good first impression of what you are trying to find out. Completing a number of graded scoring surveys in an area is a useful way of identifying differences and making comparisons.

The following examples show simple scoring surveys which could be used to collect different types of data.

You can use this technique and construct your own scoring survey to fit your investigation.

Noise pollution

Noise level	Description
1	Can hear a whisper.
2	Can hold a normal conversation.
3	Have to raise voice to be heard.
4	Difficulty hearing conversation.

Footpath erosion

Level of damage	Description
1	No evidence of damage.
2	Some evidence of damage.
3	Generally worn.
4	Serious damage / hazardous.

Traffic congestion

Traffic movement	Description
1	Traffic moving freely.
2	Minor hold-ups at junctions.
3	General congestion.
4	Considerable congestion.

Water pollution

Water quality	Description
1	No evidence of pollution.
2	Some evidence of pollution.
3	Generally polluted.
4	Highly polluted.

Good Idea

You can give more detail by explaining the descriptors in your grid. For example, in the water pollution grid:
'No evidence of pollution' means that the water is clear and there are a lot of plants and animals evident, whereas 'highly polluted' means that the water is totally cloudy with surface pollution and no evidence of plant and animal life.'

What are the advantages of using simple scoring surveys?

- A lot of information can be gathered quickly, without the use of equipment.
- It can give a useful first impression and can then be developed further if the information appears to be important.
- While it might not always be easy to identify the difference between one number and the next (1 and 2 etc.), it should be easy to see the difference between the extremes in the grid.

© Pearson Education Ltd, 2010

What are the limitations of using simple scoring surveys?

- They are not very scientific and can lack accuracy.
- It may not be easy to judge between levels.
- Judgements are subjective – different people may have different opinions!

Presenting scoring survey data

Simple scoring survey data can be presented in a table of figures. However, it is much better to use a map where you can show exactly where it was collected. A proportional symbol map like the one shown here is a useful technique.

Water pollution

OVER TO YOU:

For your investigation

List the types of information that you could collect using a simple scoring survey.

_____

_____

_____

_____

_____

_____

_____

_____

_____

_____

_____

_____

_____

Complete the following data collection grid for one type of information that you could collect using a simple scoring survey.

Heading:

	Description
1	
2	
3	
4	

Remember!

Explain why the information you collect is important for your investigation.

Good Advice

Do not forget to mention the advantages and limitations of data collection methods in your methodology and evaluation.

© Pearson Education Ltd, 2010

Using more detailed scoring surveys

Simple scoring surveys (pages 35–36) are a quick way of getting basic information from a number of places. Sometimes this may be all that is needed for an investigation. However, if detailed or specific information is needed, a more complex scoring / ticking survey might be useful.

The following examples show two different types of scoring / ticking surveys, each of which could be modified to suit different investigations.

An amenity index survey

Used to assess the functions in different settlements in a rural area.

Function	Settlement A	Settlement B	Settlement C	Settlement D
Post Office	✓		✓	✓
Supermarket			✓	✓
Clothes shop				
Hairdressers			✓	✓
Newsagents	✓	✓	✓	✓
Travel agent				
Bank				✓
Cinema				
Police station				✓
Bus / train station				✓
Doctors			✓	✓
Dentist				✓
Primary school	✓		✓	✓
Secondary school				✓

What are the advantages of using more detailed scoring surveys?

- They can give a more accurate and complete picture.
- They can include a wider range of information.
- They can include more objective data.

Ticks or numbers could be used (i.e. if a settlement has two supermarkets a number 2 would be put in the column). Ticks show whether a settlement has the function or not. Numbers show the total number of functions.

The list of functions could be changed to suit the investigation.

Presentation

The total number of functions in each settlement could be added up and the totals presented using a proportional symbol map (page 36).

© Pearson Education Ltd, 2010

Residential quality index

Used to assess the quality of different residential areas in a town.

	1	2	3	4
	Very poor	Poor	Average	Good
Quality of decoration (paintwork, etc.)				
General maintenance (windows / fences, etc.)				
Garden (tidiness)				
Quality of open spaces (Green areas / play areas)				
Traffic safety (volume of cars / parking, etc.)				

A total residential quality score can be calculated by adding up the five individual scores for each area. The lowest possible Residential Quality Score would be 5, the highest would be 20.

A residential quality index is a useful way of getting sensitive information and can assess a range of factors. However, the information can be rather subjective unless specific factors are used.

Presentation

Total residential quality scores could be presented using a proportional symbol map (see page 36).

Good Idea

The use of annotated photographs is helpful when comparing different areas.

A small number of photographs could be included on a proportional symbol map.

OVER TO YOU:

For your investigation

1 List the types of information that you could collect using a detailed scoring / ticking survey:

2 Explain why any two types of information that you have listed would be useful for your investigation:

1

2

© Pearson Education Ltd, 2010

Assessing environmental quality

Environmental quality assessment is not just about the countryside! It can be used to make judgements about a number of factors, including:

- the general quality of urban areas
- the quality of specific urban functions (parks / play areas / streets)
- different residential areas in a town
- the impact of industry on a local area
- the impact of housing and tourism developments in rural areas.

One of the easiest ways of visually assessing environmental quality is by using a technique called 'bi-polar analysis'. (Bi-polar means 'two poles' or opposites.)

How do you use bi-polar analysis?

1 Think about what it is you want to assess.
2 Work out the positive and negative aspects of each category you use to make your assessment.

For example, if you want to compare the environmental quality of different parts of a town centre, the bi-polar grid below might be useful.

Positive pole	+3	+2	+1	0	-1	-2	-3	Negative pole
Low level of traffic noise		✓						High level of traffic noise
No litter					✓			Lots of litter
Attractive buildings		✓						Unattractive buildings
Well maintained	✓							Poorly maintained
Landscaping/seating		✓						No landscaping / seating
Total score = +8								

3 Complete the bi-polar grid by making a visual judgement and ticking the appropriate boxes. (The stronger the impression the higher the number.) Zero suggests that there is no strong feeling one way or the other. In the example above, the area being assessed scored a total of +8, suggesting that the environmental quality is average. However, it is also clear that the area has a slight litter problem.

4 You can analyse bi-polar data by:
- looking at the total grid score for a place
- comparing total grid scores from a number of different places
- looking at the scores for individual categories within the bi-polar grid.

Remember!

Environmental quality data is often subjective (based on opinion rather than fact). This might be considered a weakness in its reliability as a source of data. You should mention this in your evaluation.

Good Ideas

- It is also helpful to use a map to show where your bi-polar data was collected.
- Using an annotated photograph alongside a bi-polar grid is a useful way of highlighting positive or negative points.

© Pearson Education Ltd, 2010

Presenting enviromental quality data

1 A proportional symbol map (page 36) could be used to compare different bi-polar scores in an area.

2 Bi-polar graphs can be used to:

a compare different places (in this case places A-E)

b Compare the views of different people (here each line is one person)

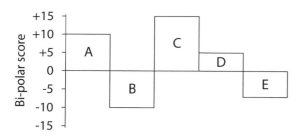

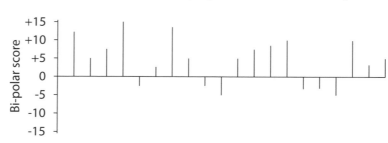

3 Using photographs with your bi-polar survey data is a good way of linking the bi-polar score with the actual area being assessed. It also means that the positive and negative points can be identified using annotations.

Good Ideas

- Bi-polar surveys can be carried out individually or by a number of people in order to get a range of opinions
- You can carry out bi-polar surveys by using photographs of areas.

OVER TO YOU

Title of investigation

1 Complete the bi-polar grid below by identifying the categories that could be used to measure one aspect of the environment in your investigation.

← —— *Write in this box what you are actually assessing*

Positive pole	-3	-2	-1	0	+1	+2	+3	Negative pole
Total score								

2 Explain why this technique is useful to your investigation.

© Pearson Education Ltd, 2010

Using pedestrian surveys

Many investigations include an understanding about:

- how people behave
- how people interact with a settlement (town or village) or the natural environment.

Pedestrian Surveys

Pedestrian surveys measure human behaviour and can be a very useful source of primary data. They can be used in a number of different types of investigation, some of which are shown by the diagrams below.

Good Ideas

- Make sure pedestrian counts are conducted over the same time period.
- The number of pedestrian counts taken and the time of day will influence your results. The more data you collect, the more reliable the results will be.
- Always explain why you selected the locations to conduct your pedestrian counts in your methodology section.

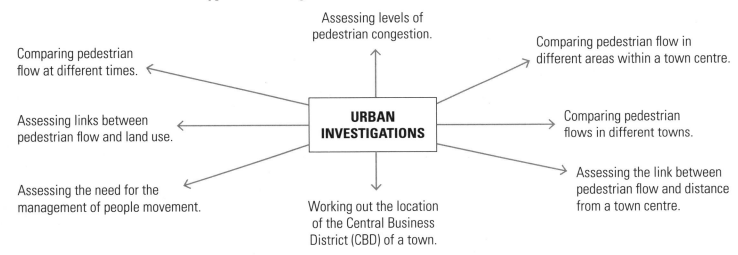

Assessing levels of pedestrian congestion.

Comparing pedestrian flow in different areas within a town centre.

Comparing pedestrian flow at different times.

Assessing links between pedestrian flow and land use.

Assessing the need for the management of people movement.

URBAN INVESTIGATIONS

Comparing pedestrian flows in different towns.

Assessing the link between pedestrian flow and distance from a town centre.

Working out the location of the Central Business District (CBD) of a town.

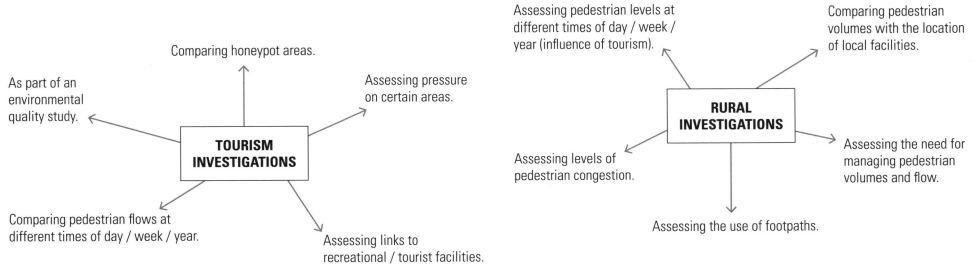

Comparing honeypot areas.

As part of an environmental quality study.

Assessing pressure on certain areas.

TOURISM INVESTIGATIONS

Comparing pedestrian flows at different times of day / week / year.

Assessing links to recreational / tourist facilities.

Assessing pedestrian levels at different times of day / week / year (influence of tourism).

Comparing pedestrian volumes with the location of local facilities.

RURAL INVESTIGATIONS

Assessing levels of pedestrian congestion.

Assessing the need for managing pedestrian volumes and flow.

Assessing the use of footpaths.

© Pearson Education Ltd, 2010

Pedestrian surveys might also be useful when:

- investigating the use of recreational areas such as beaches, riverside walkways or footpaths
- investigating the use of environmentally protected areas such as nature reserves, forest parks or other protected ecosystems.

Good Idea

Do not forget that pedestrian surveys can be linked to environmental quality surveys. An area with a lot of pedestrians may be noisy or have litter problems, etc.

Presenting pedestrian survey data

Two different ways of presenting pedestrian survey data are shown below.

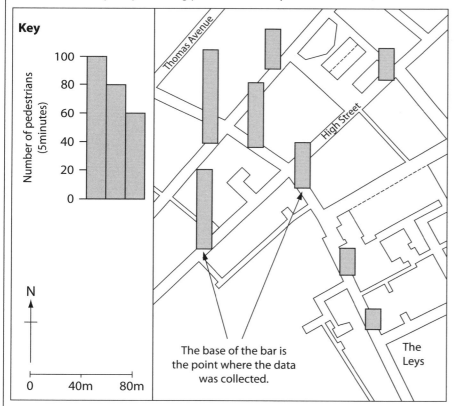

Key

Number of pedestrians (5minutes)

100
80
60
40
20
0

N

0   40m   80m

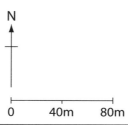

The base of the bar is the point where the data was collected.

The Leys

Key

1. Plot your pedestrian flow numbers on a map.

2. Join up the same (or approximate) numbers as isolines.

3. Shade in your map to construct a choropleth map: the higher the number, the darker the shading.

N

0   40m   80m

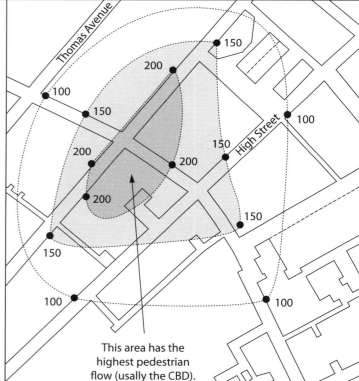

This area has the highest pedestrian flow (usually the CBD).

To show the direction of pedestrian movement a flow line map could be used (see page 44).

© Pearson Education Ltd, 2010

OVER TO YOU

Title of investigation

1   How might pedestrian surveys be useful for your investigation?

2   Use the space here to identify where / when you might collect pedestrian survey data (use a rough sketch map of your study area).

© Pearson Education Ltd, 2010

Using vehicle surveys

Traffic flow data and parking surveys can be a useful source of primary data in many different types of investigation. The following diagram shows ways that vehicle surveys can be used:

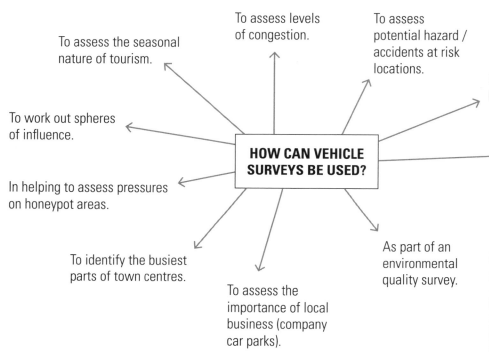

To assess levels of congestion.

To assess potential hazard / accidents at risk locations.

To assess the seasonal nature of tourism.

To work out spheres of influence.

In helping to identify the Central Business District of towns.

HOW CAN VEHICLE SURVEYS BE USED?

To assess parking problems.

In helping to assess pressures on honeypot areas.

To identify the busiest parts of town centres.

As part of an environmental quality survey.

To assess the importance of local business (company car parks).

Safety First

- Always choose safe places to collect traffic data.
- Work in pairs when collecting traffic and parking data.

Good Ideas

- If you need to compare traffic data make sure you use the same survey sites and times.
- When completing traffic surveys make a note of:
  - the general conditions (weather)
  - levels of congestion

  These factors might affect your results:
- Remember – traffic congestion adds to air pollution so could be an important environmental quality factor.

Presenting vehicle survey data

Flow line maps are a good way of showing traffic flows. The width of the line is drawn in proportion to the number of vehicles and an arrow shows the direction of flow.

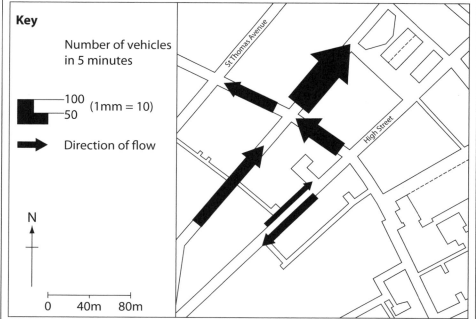

Key

Number of vehicles in 5 minutes

100
50 (1mm = 10)

Direction of flow

St Thomas Avenue

High Street

N

0   40m   80m

Traffic flow surveys

Traffic flow surveys record the total flow of traffic or the different types of traffic using particular roads. Constructing a data collection sheet, like the one below, will make data collection easier and more accurate.

Date		Time		
Location		Weather		
Cars	Motorcycles	Lorries / vans	Buses / coaches	Bicycles
ЖНŤ ЖНŤ ЖНŤ ЖНŤ ЖНŤ ||	ЖНŤ ||	ЖНŤ ЖНŤ ЖНŤ ||	|||	ЖНŤ	

© Pearson Education Ltd, 2010

Car parking surveys

Car parking surveys are frequently used as a source of data in urban investigations. However, they are also useful in rural, tourism and honeypot area investigations. They can give a useful indication to:

- parking problems
- congestion / overcrowding issues
- the effectiveness of parking management (are there sufficient car parks, are they in the right place, etc?).

Presenting car parking data

A proportional symbol map could be used to present car parking data.

Tax disc survey

Vehicle tax discs have written on them the name of the place where they were purchased. By looking at tax discs you can identify where vehicles may have come from. This could help you to identify the sphere of influence of areas, tourist areas or large shopping centres. (Ignore the tax discs issued centrally by the DVLA!)

Presenting tax disc information

A car park tax disc survey of twenty cars was carried out at Castleton – in the Peak District National Park. The desire line map was produced using the data collected by the survey.

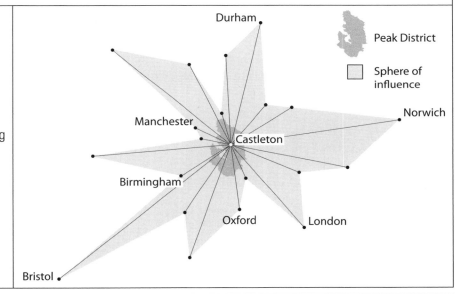

Sphere of influence

The area over which a place has influence (attracts people).

Safety First

Be careful, some people do not like their cars being looked at too closely!

OVER TO YOU

Title of investigation

Explain how vehicle flow surveys, car parking surveys or tax disc surveys might be useful for your investigation?	
Use the space here to identify the places/times you might collect the data.	

© Pearson Education Ltd, 2010

Assessing land use

A land use survey is a way of assessing the way that land is used in an area and can be either primary or secondary data.

Primary data   - if you complete your own land use survey.

Secondary data   - if you obtain a land-use map / land use information from a secondary source (local authority planning department, estate agent, Ordnance Survey).

Good Idea

You can often get useful base / street maps from the local authority planning office, Ordnance Survey or local estate agents.

Land use surveys can provide useful information for different types of geographical investigation, including:

Urban investigations

- looking at land use planning and issues such as the management of traffic and people
- comparing the land use of a local area with urban models
- looking at shopping quality and shopping patterns
- investigating land use change / urban redevelopment.

Rural investigations

- looking at social and economic functions and opportunities in rural areas
- considering the impact of change in rural settlements
- comparing the functions of rural settlements.

Tourism investigations (including National Parks)

- looking at the influence / importance of tourism in an area
- considering how the range and type of tourist facility might attract visitors
- considering the balance between facilities for local people and visitors in an area.

There are three main types of land use survey:

1   General land use survey

This type of land use survey identifies the basic types of land use in an area (commercial, residential, industrial etc.).

It is not particularly accurate, but gives a useful impression of the overall pattern of land use and the relative importance of different areas.

The opposite example identifies and shows the location of the main types of land use in a tourist resort.

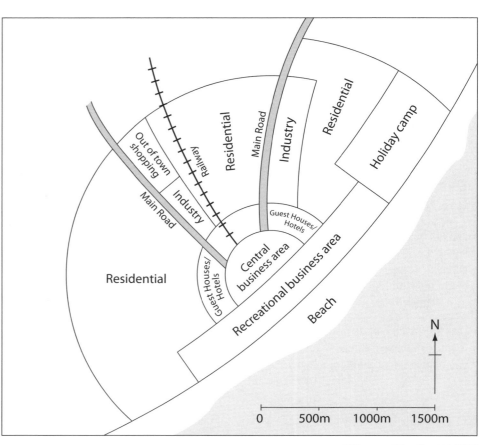

© Pearson Education Ltd, 2010

2 Detailed land use survey

This type of land use survey identifies the use of particular buildings or types of shops and services (usually on the ground floor). A detailed land use survey is helpful when completing investigations about shopping habits, identifying Central Business Districts (CBD) or topics linked to the management of town centres.

Carrying out a detailed land use survey:

In a rural area or small settlement it might be possible to identify every building. However, in urban areas you will not be able to show every different type of shop or service. You will have to identify the main categories of shop / service (especially the ones that are important to your investigation).

The following example shows a town centre land use map.

Key
- Banks / building societies / Post Office
- Estate agents / travel agents
- Clothes / shoes
- Leisure (cafes / bars)
- Supermarkets / food
- Bookshops
- Department stores

HIGH STREET

ST JAMES

N

0   100m   200m

Good Idea

If you need to break down residential areas into different categories such as type (houses/flats etc.) or value (price), information from property pages in local newspapers or estate agents might be useful.

OVER TO YOU
Title of investigation

1 Investigations about urban areas often include a land use survey as a common data collection method. Completing a second land use survey, perhaps identifying national / local businesses, or different functions, might be a way of including useful individual data. How might a land use survey (or additional land use survey) be useful to your investigation?

2 Use this space to plan your own land use survey. Think about:
- Where might you get a base map?
- What types of information might you include?
- How you might carry out your survey?
- How you might present your data?

© Pearson Education Ltd, 2010

3 Land use transect

A land use transect is a survey along a line or road. It is a useful way to see how buildings and land use change with distance from a particular point. Land use along a transect can be shown on a map. However, the use of an annotated sketch or photograph will give a clearer impression of change. If you use a sketch or photographs, make sure the position of your transect is located on a map. The example below shows how land use changes as you move from the centre of a town in one particular direction.

Good Idea

When completing a land use transect always make sure you have some idea of the scale, including the relative size of the buildings. There may be a relationship between the width and height of buildings and the distance from a town centre.

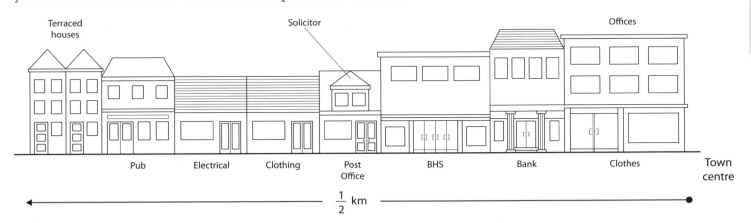

Terraced houses · Solicitor · Offices

Pub · Electrical · Clothing · Post Office · BHS · Bank · Clothes · Town centre

$\frac{1}{2}$ km

OVER TO YOU

Title of investigation

Land use transects can be used in a variety of different investigations.

1 Do you think one or more land use transects would be a useful source of information in your investigation?
   If so, explain why.

2 For your investigation, explain how you might carry out a survey in order to produce a land use transect.
   Think about where your survey should start and end and how you might get some idea of scale.

© Pearson Education Ltd, 2010

Using cross-sections

Cross-sections are a useful way of showing physical landscapes. The following three examples show how they can be used in different types of investigation.

A coastal investigation – beach profiles

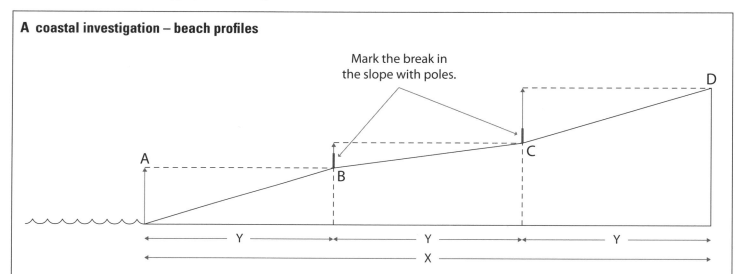

Mark the break in the slope with poles.

1 Measure the width of the beach (**X**).
2 Mark the main breaks in slope and measure the distance between them (**Y**).
3 Using a clinometer (angle measurer), or by eye, work out the height at point A which would make it horizontal to point B.
4 Repeat this process up the slope to points C and D.
5 Present the data as a cross-section making sure that the vertical scale is not over exaggerated.

Good Idea

Use annotated photographs to help you describe and explain physical landscapes.

Safety First

Coastal and river environments can be dangerous. Discuss with your teacher and parents what you are doing and do not work alone.

Be aware of particular sea or river conditions:
- slippery and jagged rocks
- instability of cliff faces / slopes
- rapid change in waves / river flow
- tide timetables.

Develop this idea

Carrying out profiles at regular intervals along a beach (especially between groynes) may be a useful way of showing evidence of longshore drift.

© Pearson Education Ltd, 2010

B River Investigation – river cross-profiles

1 Measure the width of the river between the river banks (**A**).
2 Measure the depth of the river at regular intervals (**B**).
3 Present the data as a cross section making sure that the vertical scale is not over exaggerated.
4 For extra information you could measure the wetted perimeter (**C**).

Safety First

Measuring the cross-profile of a river must be done using safety equipment and under proper supervision. Only small streams / rivers should be used and never under flood conditions.

Develop this idea

Carrying out cross-profiles at different points downstream will be a useful way of identifying changes to the river channel.

OVER TO YOU

Title of investigation

If you are carrying out a coastal or river investigation, use this space to:

• identify the information that might be useful to your investigation
• consider how the information might be collected
• think about any potential problems or limitations of your data collection methods.

Habitat / Ecosystem investigations

Using a transect or cross-section is a useful way to show how plant life changes with slope (from the sea, a river, or simply across a slope). The process of measuring the slope can be done by using the technique for measuring a beach profile (page 50).

However, if the transect is over a long distance use an Ordnance Survey map to:

1 Identify the precise line of the transect.

2 Identify any breaks in the slope using the contour pattern and the scale of the map.

3 Work out the precise slope by using the contours of the map.

4 Walk along the line of the transect on the ground, identifying the different plants / habitats.

5 Present the data as an annotated cross-section making sure that the vertical scale is not over exagerated.

Good Idea

This is a useful comination of both Primary evidence (data) and Secondary information (Ordnance Survey map). It could be developed further with the use of annotated photographs.

Research

A lot of useful information about coasts / rivers and general environments can be obtained from the Environmental Agency www.environmental-agency.gov.uk

OVER TO YOU

Title of investigation

Geographical Investigations about physical geography topics are often quite visual. Consequently, photographs can be an excellent source of information. They can help you to describe features and explain processes.

Use this space to:

1 List exactly what you need each photograph to show.

- _____
- _____
- _____
- _____

2 Identify any photographs in textbooks that might be useful.

- _____
- _____
- _____
- _____

© Pearson Education Ltd, 2010

Using field sketches and photographs

Field sketches and photographs are an excellent way of showing visual information and are often very useful in physical geography investigations where there might be limited opportunities for the collection of primary data.

Field sketching

A field sketch gives you the opportunity to:

- identify important features and leave out things that are less significant
- show your interpretation of a place – how you see it
- add as much or as little detail as you like.

How to draw a field sketch

You do not need to be an artist to draw a field sketch if you follow a few simple rules.

1 Before you start always look carefully at the area you are going to sketch.
2 Decide the precise area you are going to sketch and stick to it!
3 Frame the area you want to sketch and divide it into a simple grid:
   a In a landscape you might divide it into foreground, middle ground and background.
   b In an urban area which contains lots of buildings it might be easier to divide the area into grid squares.
4 Using the grid begin by adding the boldest features such as the horizon, roads, rivers and large buildings.
5 Add the detail which is important to your investigation.
6 Use shading or colour to show slope or structure. This will also help to highlight key features.
7 Complete your sketch by adding:
   - a heading
   - details about where it was drawn
   - annotations identifying the key features.

Good Idea

Always locate the position of your field sketches or photographs on a base map. Use an arrow to show the direction you were looking when you drew the sketch or took the photograph. Use of a Geographical Positioning System (GPS) might be helpful.

Remember!

A field sketch is both a presentation skill and a means of identifying key points so it could be worth a lot of credit!

Good Advice

- When using field sketches always ask yourself:
  - In which part of my investigation will a field sketch be useful?
  - What information should I include to make the field sketch relevent to my investigation?
- Include some idea of scale (even though distance will distort it).

Good Idea

Why not base your field sketch on a photograph?
- Select a photograph.
- Draw a grid over the photograph to guide you.
- Do not include everything – pick out the most relevant points to your investigation.

The following example shows a field sketch in an investigation about river processes and features.

A meander on the River Rudd

Woodland

Flatter land – marsh

River cliff, slumping (erosion)

Tributary

River beach / slip off slope (deposition)

Faster flowing

Slower flowing

OVER TO YOU

Title of investigation

1 How might field sketches be useful in your investigation?

2 For one field sketch, suggest what information/annotations you might include.

3 Use the following space to draw a practice sketch which might be useful to your investigation. Do not forget to add annotations.

© Pearson Education Ltd, 2010

Using photographs

Photographs are an excellent source of both primary and secondary data. However, when using photographs you need to consider the following points:

- Why is the photograph useful to my investigation?
- How can the photograph be used to make particular points?
- How am I going to show where the photograph was taken and the direction the camera was pointing?

Using photographs successfully

1 Don't use too many photographs – careful selection of appropriate photographs is important.

2 Each photograph you use must make a descriptive or analytical point.

3 Make sure you refer to your photographs within the written text.

4 Just like any other visual presentation, make sure each photograph has a clear title.

Oblique aerial photographs

Aerial photographs can sometimes be found on local websites.

They can often provide an excellent front cover illustration which clearly shows the nature and location of an investigation. The following photograph was used on the cover page of an investigation about coastal processes and features. It was also included within the investigation with detailed annotations.

Good Idea

A well chosen photograph on the front cover of your investigation will not only help to 'set the scene', it is also an ICT skill!

A word of warning!

It is easy to see photographs as a 'space filler' which then makes your completed investigation look more like a photograph album rather a geographical fieldwork report!

The important thing is to 'use' the photograph to make a point and to add annotations to develop the point you are trying to make.

© Pearson Education Ltd, 2010

The following examples show how annotated photographs can be used in both human and physical investigations.

Town centre traffic management investigation

Coastal management investigation

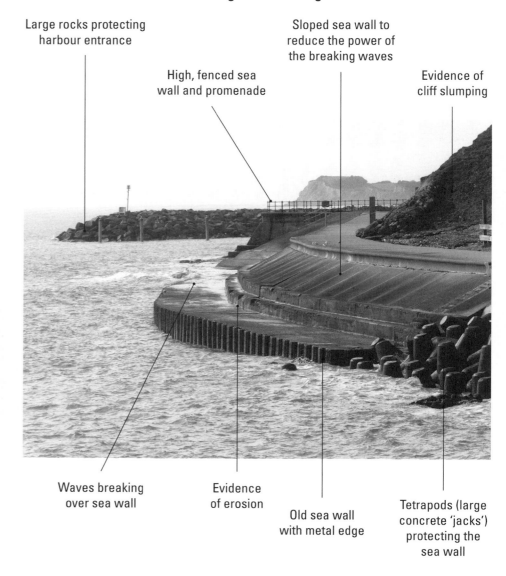

Older buildings – many with protection orders

Major bank or building society

National shops

Small pedestrianised areas around crossing point

High Street (one way)

Narrow pavements

A number of crossing points with traffic management

Parking on both sides – only narrow road area

Large rocks protecting harbour entrance

High, fenced sea wall and promenade

Sloped sea wall to reduce the power of the breaking waves

Evidence of cliff slumping

Waves breaking over sea wall

Evidence of erosion

Old sea wall with metal edge

Tetrapods (large concrete 'jacks') protecting the sea wall

© Pearson Education Ltd, 2010

OVER TO YOU
Title of investigation ....

1 List the photographs that might be useful to your investigation. Explain briefly why each photograph might be useful.

Photograph	Why it might be useful

2 Select two of your examples from (1) and note down the annotations you might use to highlight the key points.

© Pearson Education Ltd, 2010

Section 4: Organising your Controlled Assessment report

Having collected the data required, you are now ready to begin putting your report together. Before you start, you need to think about an overall structure and consider what you want your finished report to look like.

The following points might be worth considering:

Make sure your work follows the mark scheme. This will make it easier to score marks in each of the marking criteria.

A cover page with a clear title is important.

A list of contents might be helpful – but remember to number the pages!

Your work needs to be well organised and logical. All maps, graphs, photographs and diagrams should have clear titles.

Include a bibliography – list all the resources used (books, articles, websites etc.).

Use clear headings to organise and structure your report.

Include a copy of any questionnaire that has been used.

Use a number of different types of presentation, including more complex methods.

Remember!
You are producing a report, not a book! The recommended word limit is only 2000 words!

You may have taken lots of photographs. Select the photographs that are the most relevant to your investigation.

© Pearson Education Ltd, 2010

Organisation structure

The following example will give you some ideas about how you might organise your report.

Cover page

A well-presented cover page sets the scene and helps to show that your investigation is well organised.

Including the task option makes a clear link to your GCSE course content.

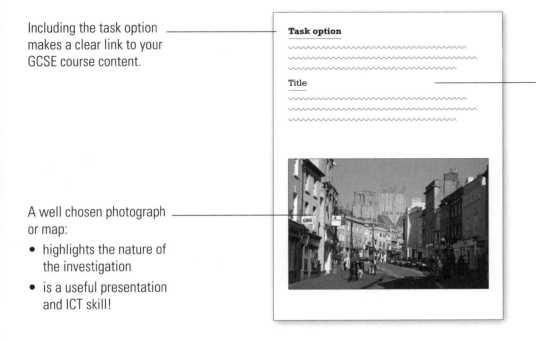

Task option

Title

A well chosen photograph or map:

- highlights the nature of the investigation

- is a useful presentation and ICT skill!

A title should:

- say exactly what the investigation is about and link it to the task option

- give some idea of location (if appropriate).

Remember!

Always remember that your cover page gives the first impression of your work.

© Pearson Education Ltd, 2010

Introduction

The first section in most investigations is an introduction, which usually:

- explains what the investigation is about
- gives some appropriate background information
- introduces the key words and ideas
- locates the investigation.

This is describing the context of the investigation —
If the investigation:

- is considering an issue or problem you need to explain what that is
- is comparing a local example with a geographical theory you need to explain the theory
- is looking at an aspect of physical geography you need to explain the main processes and features that are important.

Start by putting the title

General location map
Include:

- nearby towns
- main roads

Detailed map showing the site of the investigation with:

- annotations highlighting key points
- annotated photographs helping to set the scene.

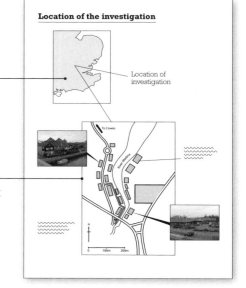

Methodology

This is a short section which describes and explains the data collection methods that have been used.

A methodology table is a useful way of describing and explaining data collection methods. It is important to:

- name the data source (traffic survey, questionnaire etc.)
- describe the method used to collect the data
- explain why the data is important to your investigation.

You could also mention any problems / limitations of each method.

It is a good idea to identify:

- group data collection methods
- individual data collection methods.

A brief introduction which:

- describes the aim of the investigation
- explains how the data collection methods are linked to the investigation, for example;

'The aim of this investigation is to consider the issues relating to an area of deciduous woodland near Winchester, in Hampshire. In order to do this a range of information about the use and management of the area will be collected. This will then be used to reach a conclusion about the major issues affecting the area.'

Examiner's comment

In the best reports once you have read the introduction it is totally clear what the investigation is about. Maps are used effectively to locate the study area, often with annotations picking out the important points.

Remember!

It is recommended that your **introduction, methodology** and **data presentation** should be approximately 800 words in length.

© Pearson Education Ltd, 2010

Presentation and interpretation

This is where you present, describe and analyse the data that you have collected.

There are two main ways of doing this.

1 Present all of the data and then write about it.

2 Present and write about each set of data separately. This is the most commonly used method. An example of what this might look like is shown here.

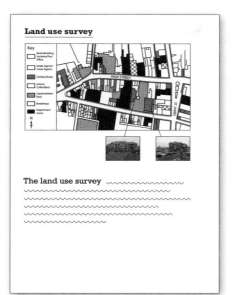

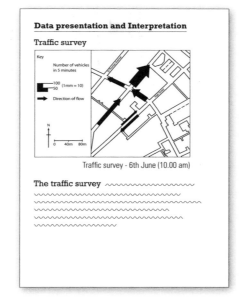

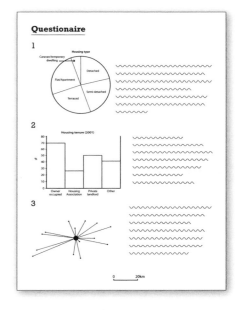

Every investigation must have a conclusion where you return to the original idea and draw everything together.

If you present each data set separately it is not always easy to identify the links between the sets of data. A summary interpretation, picking out the most important points and identifying links between the data might be helpful.

Examiner's comment

In the best investigations candidates describe and explain their data and identify detailed links between the data sets. They then link the key points from the data to the original title and use these to come to a sound conclusion.

© Pearson Education Ltd, 2010

Evaluation

This is where you have the opportunity to comment on how well your investigation worked.

There are three parts to the evaluation.

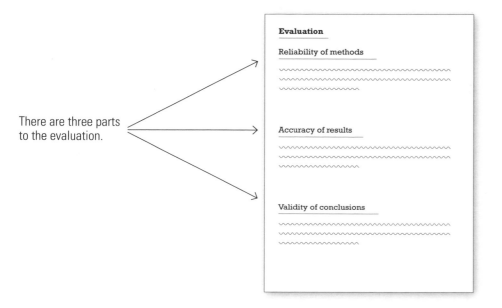

Evaluation

Reliability of methods

Accuracy of results

Validity of conclusions

Remember!

It is recommended that your **interpretation, conclusion** and **evaluation** should be approximately 1200 words in length.

© Pearson Education Ltd, 2010

Bibliography

Complete your work by including a bibliography. This is a list of all the sources that you have used, including books, articles, websites, etc.

OVER TO YOU

Title of investigation ....

Use this space to make a note of the sources of information that you have used.

Author	Title	Web address	Publisher	Page	Date

© Pearson Education Ltd, 2010

Getting the marks – using the marking scheme to help you succeed

This chapter looks at each area of the mark scheme and identifies some of the important points which will help you score the highest marks as you put your fieldwork report together.

Geographical understanding

Geographical understanding means that you show a general understanding about the topic and can relate this to the specific local example that you are investigating.

For example if your investigation is about features in a local river, you need to show that you have a general understanding of river processes and features and how these relate to your investigation. You can also introduce and explain any key words/terms that might be important.

Geographical understanding needs to be shown throughout your report, but it is especially important in the introduction, because it is here that you set the scene for your whole investigation.

Where and how might you show 'geographical understanding'?

In your introduction

- Identify the key words and ideas – explain the background to your investigation (what it is about).

- Show clearly the general location of your investigation.

- Include detailed information about the specific study area.

In your methodology

- State clearly the aim of your investigation.

- Say what data you need to address the aim, for example if your investigation is based around a question a useful opening statement might be: 'In order to answer the question, the following data was important...'

- Explain why the data you are using is important to your investigation.

In your interpretation

- Make sure you return to the original key ideas and use the important geographical words when you analyse your data and write your conclusion and evaluation.

Remember!

Your work will be marked using a common mark scheme which has five key areas of equal value.

- Geographical understanding
- Methodology
- Presentation
- Interpretation
- Evaluation

Remind youself about the mark scheme on page 5.

Examiner's comment

The best way to show that you understand the topic being investigated is to start by doing some background reading! Use classwork notes and textbooks to identify key words and ideas and make sure you mention these throughout your report. If your investigation is about a particular question or debate outline the main issues in your introduction.

Do not forget to make a note of any resources used during your research so you can include them in your bibliography!

© Pearson Education Ltd, 2010

Introduction

The introduction is an important part of your report. It should:

- state the aim of the investigation
- introduce the general topic and relevant geographical ideas and words
- show a clear understanding about the context of the topic (what it is about in relation to the study area)
- describe the location of the study area.

Useful techniques for your introduction

Using a definition box

A definition box is a simple way of identifying and defining the key words which are important to your investigation. It is very clear and does not waste space or words!

OVER TO YOU

Title of investigation _____

Use this space to make a note of the key geographical words that you might use in your report.

Key geographical words	Definition

Good Idea

Always put words in alphabetical order.

Locating your investigation

Geography is always about place so it is important that you locate your investigation effectively. Always think, 'If someone who does not know this area looked at my investigation, would they be able to work out exactly where it was?'

Location can be 'described', but using maps is a much better option.

Why should you use maps to locate your investigation?

1 Using maps is a clearer and easier way of showing location.
2 Using maps could be both a presentation skill and evidence of the use of ICT.
3 Using maps can save you a lot of words and fits in better with a 'report' style.
4 Maps can be annotated and used with photographs. This is a useful way of describing the most important points of your investigation.

Good Idea

Published maps can be useful but can have too much detail. Remove what you don't need and highlight what is important to your investigation.

Do not forget

Google Earth might be useful!

The following examples show how two different methods have been used to describe the location of investigations. What are the strengths and weaknesses of each method?

Remember!

To be complete a map should have:

- a title   - a north point
- a scale line   - a key

Background - Investigation about traffic problems in Alton town centre.

The location of Alton

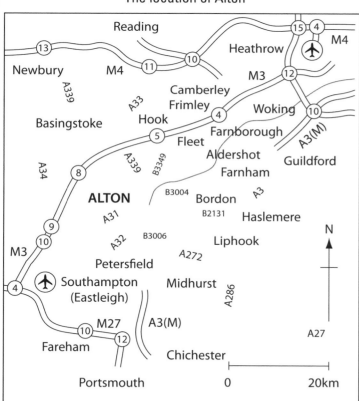

The main features of Alton town centre

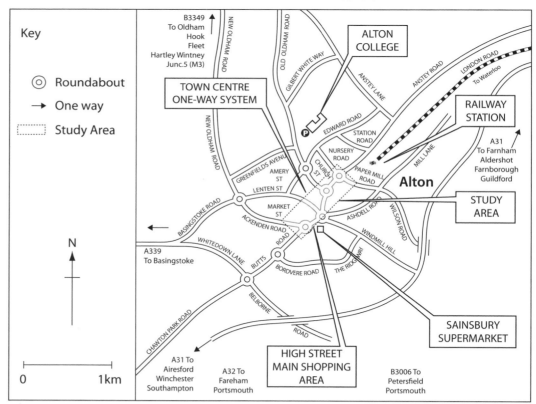

Key

- ⊚ Roundabout
- → One way
- ⋯ Study Area

Examiner's comment

It is always useful to show the general area of the investigation and also a more detailed site map of the specific study area. In this example the site map might be better if it showed a smaller area surrounding the study area. It might then be possible to include a little more detailed information linked to the investigation.

© Pearson Education Ltd, 2010

Background - Investigation about land use change / regeneration in an urban area.

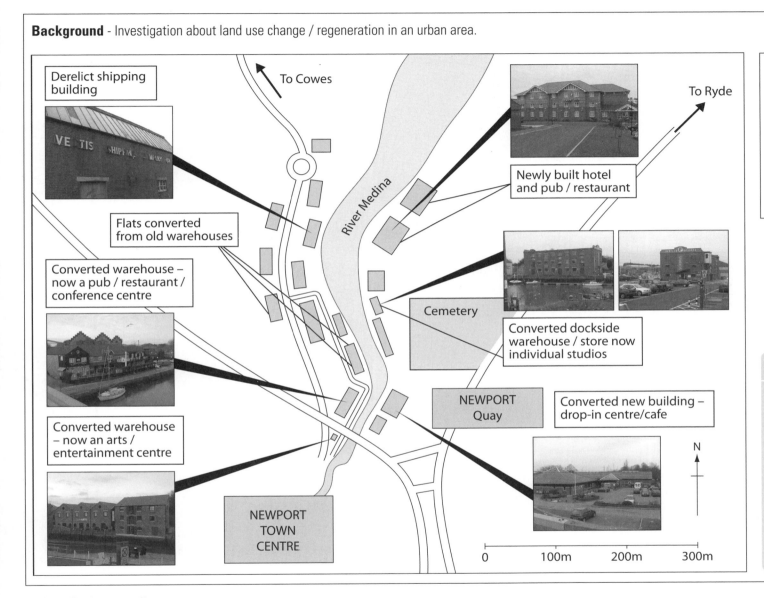

Derelict shipping building

To Cowes

To Ryde

Newly built hotel and pub / restaurant

Flats converted from old warehouses

River Medina

Converted warehouse – now a pub / restaurant / conference centre

Cemetery

Converted dockside warehouse / store now individual studios

Converted warehouse – now an arts / entertainment centre

NEWPORT Quay

Converted new building – drop-in centre/cafe

NEWPORT TOWN CENTRE

N

0   100m   200m   300m

Examiner's comment

The map gives excellent detail about the study area and clear links to the topic being investigated. It provides an opportunity for ICT skills. However, the map does not have a title or a key. There is also a need for a general location map to show the actual location of the study area.

Good Advice

- Make sure your maps show:
  - the general location of your investigation
  - detailed information about the actual study area.
- Use these two examples and the examiners comments to identify what you need to do to give clear locational background information about your study area.

Using Ordnance Survey maps

Ordnance Survey (OS) maps can be an excellent source of information and can help you produce a base map of your study area. However, simply copying or downloading part of an OS map is not really a skill!

If using an OS map it might be better to modify the map by removing information that is not relevant. You could also add annotations to identify important points which are clearly linked to your investigation.

© Pearson Education Ltd, 2010

OVER TO YOU

Title of investigation _____

Use this space to complete a rough draft of the written parts of your introduction.

_____
_____
_____
_____
_____
_____
_____
_____
_____
_____
_____
_____
_____
_____
_____
_____
_____
_____
_____
_____

List all the information you need to include on the map showing the study area.

- _____   - _____
- _____   - _____
- _____   - _____
- _____   - _____

© Pearson Education Ltd, 2010

Notes

Use this space to make any additional notes about your **INTRODUCTION** section.

© Pearson Education Ltd, 2010

Methodology

Methodology is about explaining the importance of the data collection methods to your investigation **and** showing that your work is well planned and well organised. In order to do this you need to:

1 Write a brief introduction which describes the sequence of the investigation. This should:
   - identify the general topic being investigated
   - state the specific aim of the investigation
   - briefly explain that:
     • data is needed to address the aim
     • the data will be presented in a visual form
     • the data is required in order to reach a conclusion
     • it is important to evaluate the whole process.

2 Describe and explain the methods of data collection, making sure that you:
   - describe how each method was carried out
   - explain why each method is important to your investigation
   - mention any factors that may have influenced the results (weather / time of day, week etc.)
   - consider how the data collection methods might be developed / improved.

Useful methodology techniques

Methodology table

A methodology table is a way of listing the data collection methods and explaining how they were carried out. The following example shows part of a methodology table for a town centre based investigation.

Method	Description	Importance of data	Problems / limitations	Possible development
Pedestrian survey	Ten sites were chosen at 100m intervals across the town centre. People passing were counted for five minutes during a weekday (mid-afternoon).	• Important to identify how busy different parts of the town centre are. • Investigate the link between pedestrian numbers and the location of car parks.	• It was unusually wet and cold so numbers may have been reduced. • Building work made counting in two locations difficult. • Narrow range of data.	• Data at different times of day / days of week might give a clearer picture. • Another four sites might give clearer results for the whole town centre.

Always try to give some idea about sampling decisions, i.e.:
   - numbers of people
   - types of people
   - numbers of survey sites
   - location of survey sites.

Make sure that you clearly identify any individual data collection methods that you used.

Remember!

1 Your investigation **must** include primary data to get beyond Level 1 in the marking criteria.

2 To reach Level 3 in the marking criteria **at least one** data collection method must be original **and** it must make a clear contribution to your investigation.

Remind yourself about the marking criteria on page 4.

Examiner's comment

Methodology tables are an excellent way of showing the what, why and how of the methods used, but you must make sure that you include enough detail to get the highest marks!

© Pearson Education Ltd, 2010

Methodology map

If most of the primary data is collected in a relatively small area a methodology map is a useful way of showing the general location of the data collection points. The following example shows a methodology map for an urban investigation about managing people and traffic movement. It clearly highlights the different types of data that was collected and shows the data collection points in relation to the town centre. If more explanation is required, annotations could be added.

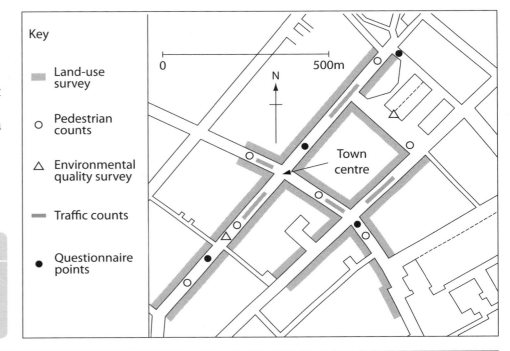

Key

▬ Land-use survey

○ Pedestrian counts

△ Environmental quality survey

▬ Traffic counts

● Questionnaire points

Town centre

0   500m

N

Examiner's comment

A methodology map is also a presentation skill and could be used with annotated photographs to highlight important points.

Good Idea

Geographical Positioning Systems (GPS) could be used to show the precise location of data collection sites!

OVER TO YOU

Title of investigation _____

Use this space to rough out a brief introduction to your methodology using the points on page 70 (Point 1)

_____

_____

_____

_____

_____

_____

_____

_____

_____

_____

_____

_____

Explanation of questionnaires

Most investigations use questionnaires as a source of primary data. A questionnaire summary, like the one below, can be used to explain the importance of the questionnaire to the investigation.

This question gives information about the stability of the population and rate of change.

People who do not have a car may need more local transport services.

This will give an idea about what people want. It is a mixture of shops and social services — the importance of each can be judged using this information.

INVESTIGATION ABOUT THE SERVICES IN A LOCAL VILLAGE

1 How long have you lived in the village?
☐ 0–5 years   ☐ 6–10 years
☐ 11–15 years   ☐ 16+ years

2 Do you travel to work outside the village each day?
☐ Yes   ☐ No

3 Do you own a car?
☐ Yes   ☐ No

4 Do you feel that the local services in the village are adequate?
☐ Yes   ☐ No

5 Which of the following services would you like to see in the village?
Garage ☐   Hairdresser ☐
Library ☐   Food shop ☐
Doctor's surgery ☐
Primary school ☐
Others (please list) _____

People who travel outside the village may rely less on local services.

This will give a general impression about people's views.

Make sure that when carrying out questionnaires you always explain the sample size (the number of questionnaires) and how / why you selected the particular respondents.

OVER TO YOU
Title of investigation _____

If you have used a questionnaire, write a brief justification for each question.

_____

_____

_____

_____

_____

© Pearson Education Ltd, 2010

OVER TO YOU
Title of investigation _____

Use this space to draft out a methodology table. Make sure you mention each method of data collection you have used and identify any individual methods you have used.

Notes

Use this space to make any additional notes about your **METHODOLOGY** section.

© Pearson Education Ltd, 2010

Presentation

Presentation is about:

- the visual methods used to present data (graphs, maps, tables, photographs etc.)
- the neatness and accuracy of the presentation methods
- the use of ICT to present and interpret data.

What is meant by 'accurate and complete'?

This means that:

- all presentations should have a title
- graphs should be of appropriate type with an appropriate scale and they should be drawn neatly and accurately
- maps should have scales, north points and keys where appropriate
- statistical calculations should be correct with all working shown.

Building up a range of presentation methods

Presentation methods can be used throughout your report. The following examples are just a few of the possibilities.

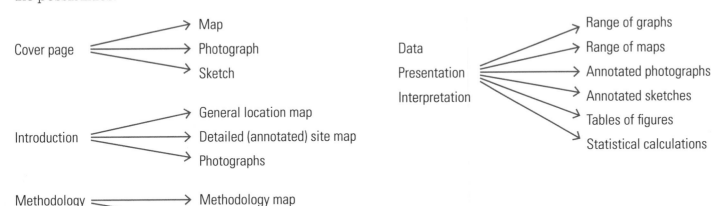

Cover page → Map, Photograph, Sketch

Introduction → General location map, Detailed (annotated) site map, Photographs

Methodology → Methodology map, Photographs

Data Presentation Interpretation → Range of graphs, Range of maps, Annotated photographs, Annotated sketches, Tables of figures, Statistical calculations

© Pearson Education Ltd, 2010

Examiner's comment

To score highly in this section you need to use a range of appropriate presentation techniques that are accurate and complete. At least two more complex skills must be used to reach Level 3 in the mark scheme (page 5).

Remind yourself about the marking criteria on page 4.

Remember!

- If there is no use of ICT you will not get many marks for presentation.
- Word processing does not count as an ICT skill in the marking criteria.

Good Ideas

- Use the 'collecting and presenting information' section to get ideas for data presentation methods.
- Look through textbooks to get ideas about presentation methods.

What are 'more complex presentation skills'?

The following presentation skills may be regarded as 'more complex' if they are appropriate, accurate and complete:

- choropleth maps
- isoline maps
- proportional symbol maps
- proportional flow line maps
- annotated cross-sections/beach profiles
- located field sketches and photographs with detailed annotations
- accurate scattergraphs (with best fit line)
- statistical techniques (where all the working is shown).

Good Advice

Sometimes skills are only 'complex' if they are used in detail. For example, using photographs with simple headings and no real locational understanding is quite a basic skill. However, using located and fully annotated photographs is a more complex skill.

OVER TO YOU

Title of investigation _____

Use this space to create a checklist of the presentation skills that you might use.

	Presentation skills
Cover page	
Introduction	
Methodology	
Presenting data	
Interpretation	

Have you identified:

1 A range of presentation skills?

2 At least two 'more complex' presentation skills?

© Pearson Education Ltd, 2010

Notes

Use this space to make any additional notes about your **PRESENTATION** section.

© Pearson Education Ltd, 2010

Interpretation

Interpretation is where you describe, explain and analyse the results of your data collection and reach a conclusion in relation to the aim of your investigation.

Responding to the mark scheme

In order to score high marks for your interpretation you need to do exactly what is required in the mark scheme (page 5). The following guidance may help you:

Level 1 (1 – 4 marks)

- Simple description of data using basic terminology (bigger/smaller/many/most/few/lots).
- Basic reasons/statements: *'Lots of people are found in the town centre because of all the shops'.*
- Some use of geographical language.

Level 2 (5 – 8 marks)

- More precise description of data, using figures/facts: *'78 per cent of people visited the town centre to shop'.*
- Explanation/Analysis backed up by evidence from the data.
- Offers a conclusion which is linked to the original aim of the investigation.
- Range of geographical terms used.

Level 3 (9 – 12 marks)

- Describes, explains and analyses data in detail with clear evidence used to make points.
- Identifies links between data.
- Detailed conclusion based on evidence. Conclusion clearly linked to original aim of the investigation.
- Wide range of geographical terms used.

The importance of a proper conclusion

The conclusion gives you the opportunity to:

- show understanding by making sure that you return to the original aim of the investigation
- identify the most significant evidence from the data collection
- identify important links between the different data sets.

If the investigation is:

- **a question** – make sure that you have answered it
- **a hypothesis** – make it clear whether it has been proven or not
- **an issue** – make sure that you have identified all sides of the argument
- **linked to theory** – make sure you draw a clear comparison with the original theory.

Don't forget QWC!

'Quality of Written Communication' can be used to adjust your mark in this section so check your spelling and grammar before you give your work in!

What is meant by 'analyse'?

Analyse means more than just explaining the data. It means breaking the data down and picking out the most important parts in relation to the title of the fieldwork investigation.

Good Idea

It is useful to:
- use a clear sub-heading to start your **conclusion**
- start your conclusion by re-stating the aim of your investigation:

"The aim of this investigation was..."

Examiner's comment

The most successful reports identify the main points from the data and suggest clear reasons for the results or the data collection. They then go on to identify the important links between the data and use these to return to the original idea to reach a conclusion, which is clearly linked to the original aim of the investigation.

© Pearson Education Ltd, 2010

Useful interpretation techniques

The following methods are ways of helping to explain the results of data collection.

Using tables

Tables are a useful way of summarising questionnaire data. The following examples show how they can also be used to identify the key points in relation to a question or issue.

Investigation about pedestrianisation in a town centre.

Advantages of pedestrianisation	Disadvantage of pedestrianisation
Will make the area safer.	Will cost a lot of money.
Improve the shopping environment.	Disruption while being put in place.

Investigation considering different methods of traffic management.

Method	+	−
One way system.	Faster traffic flow.	Confusing. Requires road changes.
Increase number of traffic lights.	Slows traffic so: • safer • fewer accidents.	May increase congestion.

Using statistics

Data is often collected in the form of numbers (statistics). There are a number of simple ways of describing statistics, including:

- calculating averages
- calculating the median (the middle value of ranked data)
- calculating the mode (the most frequently occurring number)
- describing the minimum and maximum numbers
- calculating the statistical range (largest minus smallest)
- drawing a dispersion diagram.

Example of a dispersion diagram

Question - 'How often do you visit the following shopping areas each month?'

Each dot represents one person.

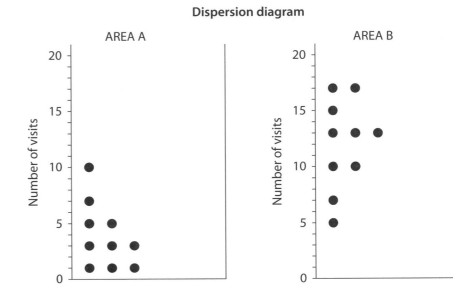

Dispersion diagram

Using statistical techniques to explain / analyse relationships between data

The following example shows how statistical techniques can be used to examine the relationship between two sets of data.

Using statistical techniques: an example of a shopping investigation

Aim: To see if the number of pedestrians decreases with the distance from a town centre.

Data collection method: Ten locations were chosen at varying distances from the town centre. At each location the number of pedestrians was counted over a five-minute period.

Collected data for shopping investigation.

Location	1	2	3	4	5	6	7	8	9	10
Distance from town centre (m)	10	50	100	80	70	200	150	400	300	250
Number of pedestrians (nearest 10)	320	280	270	260	290	200	210	90	190	170

Presenting the data as a scattergraph

To draw a scattergraph:

1 Draw and label the two axes.

2 Choose scales to cover the range of data.

3 Plot the data using dots.

4 Put on a line of best fit (do not just join up the dots!).

What does a scattergraph show?

- **Positive relationship** – as one data set increases, so does the other.
- **Negative relationship** – as one data set increases, the other decreases.
- **No relationship** – no real pattern is evident, so the relationship is unproven (a best fit line cannot really be drawn).

What does the scattergraph of the shopping investigation data suggest?

1 There is a negative relationship – the number of pedestrians falls as distance from the town centre increases.

2 It is quite a strong relationship since all the dots are close to the line of best fit.

3 Some dots do not quite fit the pattern (some explanation for this would be useful).

Good Idea

In some investigations it might be important to analyse the relationship between two sets of data. For example, in a river investigation you might collect data about the speed and depth of a river at different locations as the river flows downstream.

Statistical techniques could be used to see whether these two factors are linked (I.e. does the river flow faster where it is deeper?).

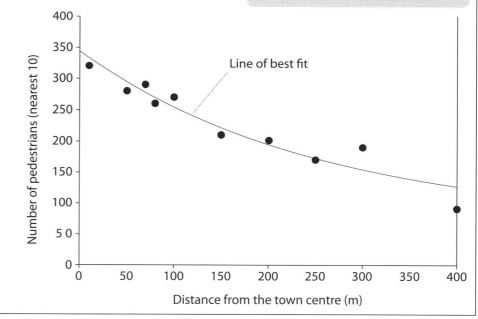

© Pearson Education Ltd, 2010

Testing the strength of a relationship

Looking at the scattergraph of the shopping investigation data on the previous page, it is clear that the two sets of data are related. The strength of a relationship between two sets of data is called a correlation. This can be calculated using the Spearman Rank Correlation Coefficient (RS). This is a statistical calculation which always gives a result from −1 (negative correlation) to +1 (positive correlation); the nearer to 1 the stronger the link between the data.

How do you calculate RS?

1 Rank both sets of data from the highest to the lowest.

Distance from town centre	Rank	Number of pedestrians	Rank	Difference between ranks (d)	d^2
400	1	90	10	9	81
300	2	190	8	6	36
250	3	170	9	6	36
200	4	200	7	3	9
150	5	210	6	1	1
100	6	270	4	2	4
80	7	260	5	2	4
70	8	290	2	6	36
50	9	280	3	6	36
10	10	320	1	9	81
					Total (Σd^2) = 324

2 Use the formula:

$$RS = 1 - \frac{6 \times \Sigma d^2}{n^3 - n}$$

Where:

n = number of observations
d = difference between ranks
Σ = total d^2

3 Using the example above:

$$RS = 1 - \frac{6 \times 324}{1000 - 10}$$

$$= 1 - \frac{1944}{990}$$

$$= 1 - 1.196$$

$$= -0.96$$

4 This shows that there is a very strong negative relationship between the number of pedestrians and the distance from the town centre. In other words as you move away from the town centre the number of pedestrians decreases.

© Pearson Education Ltd, 2010

OVER TO YOU
Title of investigation _____

Use this space to draft out your written interpretation. When you have done it check that you have;

- identified all the major points that are linked to the original aim of the investigation
- returned to the key ideas and included relevant geographical terminology.

Use your draft to complete your final written interpretation.

Remember!

You are producing a Fieldwork Report which should not be more than 2000 words in length.

Your interpretation needs to identify the most important points from your data, but should only be a few hundred words in length!

© Pearson Education Ltd, 2010

OVER TO YOU

Title of investigation _____

Conclusion

Use this space to consider the main points of your conclusion **and** identify evidence that you might use to support those points.

Main points of conclusion	Evidence
•	•
•	•
•	•

© Pearson Education Ltd, 2010

Notes

Use this space to make any additional notes about your **INTERPRETATION** and **CONCLUSION**.

© Pearson Education Ltd, 2010

Evaluation

Evaluation is about reflecting upon how effectively the investigation process addressed the original idea and making observations about how the process could be improved or developed.

The evaluation pathway

The three elements of the evaluation pathway are shown below. It is always worth starting by looking at the methods because it is usually limitations in the methods that affect the results and conclusions.

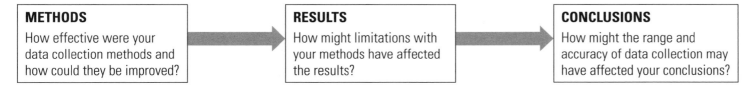

METHODS	RESULTS	CONCLUSIONS
How effective were your data collection methods and how could they be improved?	How might limitations with your methods have affected the results?	How might the range and accuracy of data collection may have affected your conclusions?

Organising the evaluation

It might be helpful to organise your evaluation into the following three sub-sections. This may help to ensure that you discuss each part of the evaluation pathway. However, make sure that you explain the links between each sub-section.

Good Idea

You could organise your evaluation as a flow chart. If you do, make sure you have enough detail in each box!

Think about the following points:

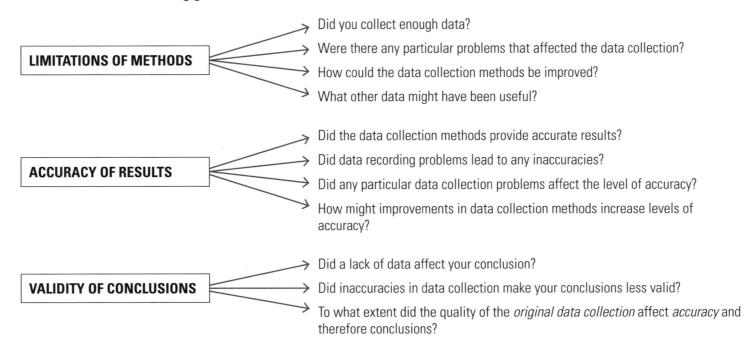

LIMITATIONS OF METHODS
- Did you collect enough data?
- Were there any particular problems that affected the data collection?
- How could the data collection methods be improved?
- What other data might have been useful?

ACCURACY OF RESULTS
- Did the data collection methods provide accurate results?
- Did data recording problems lead to any inaccuracies?
- Did any particular data collection problems affect the level of accuracy?
- How might improvements in data collection methods increase levels of accuracy?

VALIDITY OF CONCLUSIONS
- Did a lack of data affect your conclusion?
- Did inaccuracies in data collection make your conclusions less valid?
- To what extent did the quality of the *original data collection* affect *accuracy* and therefore conclusions?

© Pearson Education Ltd, 2010

Useful evaluation techniques

The following examples show techniques that can help to identify important points which could be used as part of a full evaluation.

Commenting on each data set - An evaluation grid

Method	Reliability of method	Accuracy of results	Validity of conclusion
Pedestrian flow survey.	• Quite reliable, although some people may have been missed. • Was only completed at one time.	• May have missed people or double-counted when it was busy.	• Limited data to draw detailed conclusions. • Problems of accuracy may give a false impression.

Commenting on the whole process

- Identifying problems and solutions

Problems	Solutions
• Only collecting data on a weekday may have affected the overall pattern of results.	• Collecting data at the weekend would give a more reliable impression.
• Poor weather on the day of the data collection may have affected traffic / people numbers.	• Collecting the same data on a sunny day might show if the weather makes any difference.

- Identifying strengths/weaknesses

Strengths	Weaknesses
• Good range of traffic flow data.	• Base map not up-to-date.
• Photographs clearly identify the key issues.	• Limited number of questionnaire respondents.

Remember!

Data can be objective (facts / figures) and subjective (opinions). Subjectivity may affect the reliability of data and therefore make conclusions less valid!

© Pearson Education Ltd, 2010

OVER TO YOU

Title of investigation _____

Use this space to list the key points for your evaluation. Use the completed list as background notes to help you produce your final evaluation.

© Pearson Education Ltd, 2010

Notes

Use this space to make any additional notes about your **EVALUATION** section.

© Pearson Education Ltd, 2010

Final checklist

Use the following checklist to make sure that you have responded to each of the marking criteria.

LOCATION OF INVESTIGATION

Have you used maps to show:
- The general location of your investigation?
- The detailed study area of your investigation?

BACKGROUND UNDERSTANDING

Have you:
- Included some background knowledge about the topic being investigated?
- Shown how your background knowledge is linked to your investigation?

GEOGRAPHICAL UNDERSTANDING

GEOGRAPHICAL IDEAS / CONCEPTS

Have you:
- Identified the key geographical words and ideas that are important to your investigation?
- Discussed the key ideas in your interpretation and conclusion?

© Pearson Education Ltd, 2010

AIM OF INVESTIGATION

Have you:

- Briefly identified the topic being investigated?
- Clearly stated the aim of your investigation?

METHODOLOGY

PROCESS OF INVESTIGATION

Have you:

- Briefly described the process of your investigation, i.e:
  - selecting data to address the aim
  - explained why the data is important to your investigation?

PLANNING

Have you:

- Included primary data?
- Included individual data collection methods?

ORGANISATION

Have you included:

- A clear title page?
- Section headings?
- A bibliography?

DATA COLLECTION

Have you:

- Described your data collection methods?
- Explained why the data is important to your investigation?

PRESENTATION

USE OF ICT

Have you:

- Included evidence of the use of ICT in your investigation?

ACCURACY AND COMPLETENESS

Are your data presentation methods:

- Appropriate?
- Accurate?
- Neat?
- Complete?

PRESENTATION TECHNIQUES

Have you:

- Used a range of presentation techniques?
- Used at least two complex presentation techniques?

Notes

90

© Pearson Education Ltd, 2010

DESCRIBE AND EXPLAIN

Have you:

- Described, explained and analaysed your data?
- Made detailed reference to your data in relation to the original aim of your investigation?

LINKS BETWEEN DATA

Have you:

- Identified and explained any links between sets of data?

Notes

GEOGRAPHICAL IDEAS / LANGUAGE

Have you:

- Returned to the original key idea in your interpretation and conclusion?
- Used a range of geographical words accurately?

INTERPRETATION

CONCLUSION

Have you:

- Reached a conclusion which is supported by the evidence of your data?

EVALUATION

METHODS

Have you:

- Mentioned any problems you had with your data collection methods?
- Commented on the reliability / accuracy of your data collection methods?
- Suggested how your data collection could be developed?

RESULTS

Have you:

- Made observations about the accuracy of your results?
- Suggested how problems / limitations with data collection methods may have affected results?
- Suggested how improvements could increase the accuracy of results?

CONCLUSIONS

Have you:

- Explained how problems / limitations with data collection may have affected accuracy and therefore weakened any conclusions?
- Suggested how improvements in the investigation process might make any conclusion more accurate?

© Pearson Education Ltd, 2010

Notes

© Pearson Education Ltd, 2010